CW00701401

BEING UNSTOPPABLE

The Mindset of a Great Clinician

DR FERHAN AHMED

Being Unstoppable: The Mindset of A Great Clinician
By Dr Ferhan Ahmed

Publisher: Addea Media

ISBN: 978-1-5272-8406-7

The strategies in this book are presented primarily for enjoyment and educational purposes. The information and resources provided in this book are based upon the author's professional experience and professional expertise. Any outcome is based on the author's experience and there is no guarantee that your experience will be the same or that you will have similar results.

Although the author and publisher have made every effort to ensure that the information in this book was correct at press time, the author and publisher do not assume and hereby disclaim any liability to any party for any personal or professional loss, damage or disruption caused by errors or omissions, whether such errors or omissions result from negligence, accident, or any other cause.

Dedicated to Hana and Adam

Table of Contents

Foreword ix

Acknowledgements xi

Why Read This Book? xiii

How It All Began xix

Chapter 1

Pave Your Way to Success:
Start With a Vision of Where You Want to Go 1

The Significance of a Vision 3

Cultivating a Growth Mentality 5

Vision and Purpose Go Hand-in-Hand 7

Dissecting Your Vision 8

Making Your Goals Realistic 9

Keep Your Eyes on the Big Picture But
Focus on Your Immediate Goals 10

Goals Change - That's OK 13

Chapter 2
Plan Ahead and Practice Mental Rehearsal............ 15

The Power of the Mind 16
What is Mental Rehearsal? 20
From Mental to Physical 21
Applying It To Your Work 25
Applying It To Your Colleagues 27
Choosing to Believe in Yourself 28

Chapter 3
Prioritise Learning Before Earning 31

Education is Key.. 32
Open yourself to New Information 35
Surround Yourself with Learners 38
Open Yourself to Correction 40
Double-Check Information and Advice............ 41
Discover Your Learning Style 42
Practice What You Learn.................................... 44
Share Your Knowledge 45
Finish What You Start 47

Chapter 4
Confidence and Self-Belief 49
Building Your Confidence 50
Handling the Opinion of Others 53
The Role of Humility 55
Choose Who You Listen To 58
You Are Your Greatest Partner- And
Competition 61

Chapter 5
Overcoming Challenges and Complications 64
Changing Your Mindset About Failure 66
Complications Will Arise - Prepare for Them...... 68
Develop Your Problem-Solving Skills 70
Micro & Macro Failures 72
Assuming Responsibility.. 74
Support Network - Do You Have One? 76

Chapter 6
Communication with Patients 79
The Importance of Good Communication
Skills as a Clinician 81
The Art of Listening 83

The Art of Speaking 85
The Significance of Body Language 89
Evaluate Your Communication Skills 91

Chapter 7
Leadership 94

Leading by Example 96
Leading & Collaborating 99
Leading Through Partnerships 101
Leading Beyond Limits 102
Leading and Learning 104

Chapter 8
The Importance of Mentorship 107

The Value of a Mentor 108
Pursuing Mentorship 112
Mentors and Heroes 115

Chapter 9
Giving Back: My Charity Work 117

Charity is A Challenge 118
Do It Anyway 120
The Proceeds 123

Foreword

Dr Ferhan Ahmed is one of leading implant surgeons, not only treating patients to a high standard but also routinely training other dentists both nationally and internationally.

I met Ferhan 7 years ago. We started working together in a dental practice and we eventually became business partners. As I had been delivering implant dentistry for a while, we also developed a mentor - mentee relationship over time, where I would assist him in the development of his implant dentistry skills.

As a person, Ferhan is one of the most calm, relaxed people I know. He always thinks things through carefully and is neither rash or over-emotional and he is very methodical.

He always considers others, he is such a kind and giving individual, and is always full of energy and a real drive to better himself and others around him.

He is the same in surgical dentistry as he is as an individual outside of the workplace. His reputation within his professional field is exemplary and second to none.

His leadership skills are evident, and he always shows great insight as he considers a lot of things. He is always ahead of the game, always looking out for new opportunities, and ways to open doors for himself and others.

He is a leader who has self-confidence and deep conviction in the decisions that he is making.

So if you are a clinician trying to get to the next step of your career, and you have to come to realise that it takes a certain mindset to be a great clinician then this book is for you. You will learn from one of the best clinicians in the dental and surgical implant industry. I couldn't recommend him highly enough.

Dr Abid Faqir (BDS, MFDS RCS, MSc MedSci, Implant Dentist & Entrepreneur).

Acknowledgements

Firstly, I would like to thank my wife Sumeara for her constant and unwavering support and for allowing me to do what I need to do in my journey to reach my goals.

My dad and mum, who sacrificed so much for us, their children. Thank you, dad, for instilling me with a strong work ethic. Mum, thank you for always being available to cater to our every need.

A special thanks to everybody I have met in my journey so far. To the teachers and the work colleagues—you have all played a part in my development. To my dear friends, for their support and love. Last but certainly not least, to my MENTORS for their advice, support, time, and the opportunities they made available to me. From the bottom of my heart, I am forever grateful. You have been instrumental in shaping the person I am today and making the goals I strive to achieve a reality.

Why Read This Book?

There is more to a successful career as a clinician than the degrees and titles surrounding your name. It is not solely defined by tenure or position and cannot entirely be summed up by awards and peer recognition.

Many people achieve all of those and still miss the mark.

If you are reading this, you may already have an idea that success is more than what many people think of it. Or maybe this is the first time you have been confronted with such a thought, and you know that it is the road you must walk on.

The years you have or will spend mastering the technicalities of your profession will not suffice to shape you into the well-rounded clinician you need to be. Your mastery and talents will only take you so far. Once you have reached the end of that rope, you will realize that there are other skills necessary such as leadership, resilience, and communication to carry you further.

How far, exactly, can the right mindset take you? And what economic, professional, and personal climates can you weather by possessing a mindset attuned to greatness?

To answer that, try to see which of the following scenarios fits into your present reality:

- You are a dental, medical, or allied health student or professional who wants to maximise your potential but do not know where to start;
- You feel an intense pressure and dissatisfaction because of the lofty ideas of success propagated on social media by the people in your field;
- You know that to succeed as a private practitioner, you need to have business skills as well;
- You know that dealing with patients is not an easy job, and building rapport and relationships with people - both patients and other clinicians - is crucial to your career;
- You want to earn respect and recognition;
- You want to support the lifestyle you desire;

- You need to learn to balance your career with your family life, and that is not always an easy task;
- You are sometimes held back by fear or lack of clear direction. You know you have a purpose, you just need to find it;
- You fear being scrutinised by others in your field. Perhaps you lack guidance and support;
- You want to believe that you can do this, and you want to have confidence. You want to get better at planning, visualising, and practising what you have learnt.

These are all familiar pains to anybody pursuing a career as a healthcare professional. What the right mindset does is that it drives you to search for the solution - the key to enduring the journey to success.

I am dual qualified in dentistry and medicine. I spent a total of nine years in university. After completing my studies in dentistry, I could have joined my fellow dental graduates and become financially comfortable, but I chose to further my education instead.

My decision to pursue a medical degree left me in debt. I was behind all my peers financially, but I remained focused. I was confident that I made the right decision, and I worked on the skills which I had developed to facilitate the opportunities that would improve my situation.

Today, I am much more financially secure because of this. I cultivated a positive mindset, and in the long run, I did not have to chase after opportunities. They appeared around me, and I maximised them to their full potential.

In this book, I will share with you over twenty years worth of experience and life lessons that you can utilise to propel your own career. We will cover over two decades of building relationships with clients, learning, growing within my profession, and helping other clinicians achieve the same level of success.

I sincerely believe that if you are able to cultivate the skills and the mindset of a great clinician, you can fast-track your own career into overdrive.

I spent years struggling to get to where I am now, but it need not be as long and complicated for you. The most opportune time for you to learn everything I have to share with you is during your training at university, but regardless of where you are on your journey, the best time to start is now. Right at this moment, you can make the decision to learn these skills, implement them, and aim for success.

You are not interested in quick-fixes and shortcuts. You are in it for the long haul, and you want to find out how others before you have achieved great results. This is how far (or even further) the right mindset can take you.

This book serves as the steppingstone you have been looking for. It aims to impart wisdom and practical application on the mindset of a great clinician.

I am sharing this with you in the hope that by the time you have read my book, you will have a better understanding of what it takes to become a better professional, leader, colleague, and person.

This book is for you.

How It All Began

My father came to the United Kingdom with his uncle at nine years old. At age fifteen, he left school and pursued full-time work. Sixteen hours a day, seven days a week, from six in the morning to ten in the evening, he toiled like a man well beyond his years just to provide for his family.

If there is anything I got from my father that defines me, it is his grit.

I realised this early on, being one of five siblings. There is a silent struggle that every child goes through in identifying how and where they fit in such a big family.

In my case, though, the question of 'how' was not about fitting in but standing out.

The interesting thing with my goal is that there were two ways to achieve it. The first and simpler option was to paint myself as the black sheep. Take the easy route and remove the expectations before they weighed me down.

The second was the scary route. Choosing it was like carrying my entire family on my shoulders - the reputation, the pride, and the future—all wrapped up in one decision.

When you are born into an Asian family like I was, you do not have an abundance of career choices. You can be a doctor, an accountant, or a failure. Knowing all these, I took on the scary route not only because I wanted to make my family proud, but because I was enticed by the idea of being *somebody*. What started as a decision to stand out quickly became a passion to be different in all the right ways, for all the right reasons.

The profession that gave me that impression was dentistry. From there, it seemed easy to pick out the specifics of my career. I may have even ended up in a different path if not for an encounter with a particular individual.

I recall waiting for hours outside the cold GP surgery waiting room at seven years old. When, finally, I went in to see Dr. Khan, I was turned off by his dusty, untidy room. He looked at me in the grumpiest way. He was bald, overweight and sat slouched on his office chair. There was a dismissive air about him, and I felt he had no compassion or empathy for me.

Aside from a desire to separate myself from the norm, Dr. Khan made such a poor impression that it played a role in my decision. At that age, things were pretty much black and white for me. Did I want to be like him? No. So, dentistry it was.

I do not have regrets about it and, surprisingly, my parents were accepting. I was prepared to reason out that I would still have "doctor" as a title just in case they responded to me in disappointment. I could have not been happier to hear them say they were proud of me, nonetheless.

I completed my dental degree in my home city of Glasgow in 2005. Following vocational training in general dental practice, I spent two years working as a senior house officer in oral and maxillofacial surgery.

Upon finishing my training posts in Southern General Hospital in Glasgow and in Monklands Hospital in Airdrie, I felt there was something missing. A persistent hunger for something more than what I had already achieved plagued me, and I did not know how to silence it until an idea dawned on me.

What if I could do medicine as well?

I loved the surgical aspect of dentistry, and if I had both degrees, I could become a maxillofacial surgeon. This became my end goal in that season of my life, and I was determined to reach it.

It's possible to look back now with a smile at what had been a chaotic time with night shifts, weekends on-call, struggles to pay university fees, and keep up mortgage payments. I recall waking up startled by the sound of my beeper going off in the early hours of the morning. Instead of enjoying coffee in warm surroundings, I spent the first minutes of my day defrosting my car and driving to the hospital from my accommodation block to check up on patients.

Not to mention the drive home. The struggle to stay awake is an incomparable test of mental strength and wits. Regularly, I found myself having to roll down the car window and stick my head out just to keep myself from falling asleep. At times I would be up at 4:30 a.m. to leave my weekend on call shift in Fife, Scotland, to make 9 a.m. clinics at university in Liverpool.

Medical school finished, I moved back to Scotland ready for my medical foundation years. An opportunity presented itself to purchase an oral surgery referral clinic, and I grabbed it.

I ran the clinic three Saturdays per month. These were long, intensive days of operating on patients who were difficult to manage.

The hard work paid off when I received an offer to get involved in a partnership with a vision of establishing a group of dental clinics in Scotland. Although a career in Maxfax was attractive, I was aware of the lack of autonomy I would have, and the prospect of joining this partnership was too attractive to turn down.

Finally, I was part of something big.

This venture excelled in its early stages but broke up after two and a half years. It was like waking up from a dream, and my eyes had to adjust to the glaring lights of failure's domain.

For others, it would have been justified to wallow in self-pity and doubt, but not for me.

I used this setback as a launching pad to explore alternatives. I realized that I had to continually develop my skill sets, and to do that, I had to invest in myself.

This involved traveling to many different countries including Brazil and South Africa to learn from world experts. Shifting my focus to surgical implant dentistry was a natural progression for me considering my medical background. However it was not sufficient for me to only master the technicalities. I wanted to become the best clinician I could be, so I cultivated relationships with my colleagues, which led to some of them becoming my mentors. I committed myself to the daily practice of implant dentistry to apply what I had learnt.

To this day, I ensure that I treat people with the same professional enthusiasm as I did starting out in this field. I hold on to this passion as a form of gratitude for the people who helped me sail this way, and to honour the countless times I decided not to give up.

You are on a similar journey. Maybe you are just about to take off, or your journey has already started. Wherever you find yourself today, I am glad that you have decided to pick this book as your companion.

By helping you develop the mindset of a great clinician, I am making sure the patients you will treat will receive the high-quality service they deserve. Creating this impact in your life through this small contribution of mine would be the greatest reward of my professional career.

Chapter 1

Pave Your Way to Success: Start With a Vision of Where You Want to Go

'Setting goals is the first step to turning the invisible into the visible.'

Tony Robbins

My hometown of Glasgow has two football teams: Rangers and Celtic. The rivalry between them has impacted the nation; their influence contributed to the political and social stance of the people around me.

The intensity with which they supported these clubs did not come as a surprise. I have always loved playing and watching football, and I doubt that this passion will ever go away. As I was carried along the cities' devotion to these two clubs at a young age, I knew I had to choose a side.

Picking came easily for me - Rangers was my bet.

While the majority of the people around me cheered and hollered for the Celtic, I supported Rangers with a fervour that could compete with theirs.

I've always had the tendency to go against the norm, to root for the ones I liked even if few or none shared my sentiments. And this did not bother me. I knew I could not go against my nature, and I did not want to change my preferences to suit everybody else's.

I strived to be different, and I stayed different.

Kurt Cobain said, 'I'd rather be hated for who I am, than loved for who I am not.'

That rang true for me, especially in narrowing down the choices for my profession. While the popular option was medicine, I did not have qualms about going for dentistry. It was not typical, but that was okay because I had a vision.

The Significance of a Vision

There are two things you will want to answer when forming a vision:

Where are you going as a clinician?

What are you trying to achieve?

It's easy to come up with just any answer. The difficult part is knowing whether those answers are true to your character, desires, and values.

Visions start small, and they take shape in your mind even before you are aware of it. The ones that are going to change your life are those that complement who you are. A vision based on popular opinion or that goes against your values and beliefs will either always fail or leave you unhappy.

I could have pursued the typical, more appreciated fields in medicine, but I was not afraid to pursue dentistry. It was the choice that aligned with my personality, mindset, and worldview. If that meant setting myself apart, then so be it.

I have encountered countless dentists and other professionals who commit themselves to jobs and routines but do not have any idea which direction they are bound for. They walk into the clinic, drill, clean people's teeth, and recommend treatment plans. There is comfort in this pattern of living, but nothing *more*.

The quickest way to get rid of excellence in your life and your profession is by deciding to run a race that has no direction.

You must start with a vision. Not just any kind that you can come up with to satisfy the need to have one. It is a scary process, reflecting on what truly matters to you. Many people have never done this out of fear of upsetting the norm, their families, or their friends. They have never taken the time to investigate their own beliefs, or if they have, they are afraid that what they envision for their future is unachievable.

American educator Stedman Graham, said, 'Having a vision for your life allows you to live out of hope, rather than out of your fears.'

The point of starting with a vision is not to live fearlessly, but to capture the hope through which you will overcome those fears.

So, how can you test whether the vision you have in mind right now is leading you in the right direction?

Cultivating a Growth Mentality

My decision to pursue implant dentistry emerged after my failed business partnership endeavour. Instead of analysing the setback and pointing fingers, I looked for alternatives to arrive at my intended destination.

This is how I knew I had the right vision.

The right vision is the one that pushes you to grow even after the world brings you down. It's the visualisation that strengthens you to search for new ways and to reach for new heights.

Growth might manifest differently for you. It could be working for a specific organization, getting a certain title, starting your own clinic, or gaining enough mastery in a particular field to start educating others.

Perhaps, like me, you can see yourself limiting your clinical practice to a specific area. You want to become an authority and a respected figure in your area of expertise.

Dentistry is a broad profession. It has a lot of disciplines, such as prosthodontics, endodontics, orthodontics and others. To be known as *someone* in dentistry, you must *choose* what you want to be known for and master it.

Developing an interest in a particular field is beneficial, but that does not mean you are narrowing your expertise or experiences. Even the niche or area of interest you choose can actually be quite broad in itself. Cosmetic dentistry, for example, involves short term orthodontics, whitening, and so much more.

Yes, you need to do some general dentistry first. However, while doing that, I urge you to find what excites you and subsequently focus on that. Pursuing a highly specific expertise and focusing on one area is what will lead you to where you want to be. Discover where your heart truly lies—what your true passion is. Once you find your passion, follow that path.

Engage in that discipline day in and day out and grab every opportunity to learn and practice.

I focused on implant dentistry and that is what I have been doing exclusively for over six years. Today, I am known as an implant dentist.

Whatever it is you want, the right vision will ingrain in you a growth mentality that compels you towards doing *more* and becoming *more*. This is what entices you to look forward to where your work can lead you someday.

Find out what piques your interests and makes any challenge feel worth the sacrifice, and then pursue it. That is how you will grow.

Vision and Purpose Go Hand-in-Hand

The other reason it is integral to have a vision is that it gives you a sense of purpose. Dentistry has its unique challenges, and there are times when only a sense of purpose will get you through them.

Similar to how heavy rain blurs the windshield of your car, you will make mistakes and experience failures that dim the road ahead of you. It will be difficult to take the next step but, being fully driven by your purpose, you take that road anyway.

Roy T. Bennett said, 'If you have a strong purpose in life, you don't have to be pushed. Your passion will drive you there.'

Identifying an area I wanted to focus on gave me the tenacity I needed to overcome any obstacle. Designing the right vision allowed me to cultivate a growth mindset, and I have felt a sense of purpose that has kept my momentum going to this day.

Dissecting Your Vision

If vision is the long-term path you will take, goals are the mid-term and short-term targets that lead you along the path.

My first goal was to improve my surgical skills, and then start to place dental implants. Afterwards, I planned to develop my skills in full-arch implants before proceeding to the more complex procedures. Only after achieving competency in this did I move to extra maxillary implants and complex grafting.

Name your stepping stones. It is paramount that you have a plan of action early on because a vision will always remain a vision until you know which road you are taking to get there.

If you have tried this before and you have not managed to set yourself clear goals, then perhaps you need to be more resourceful. Research what your options are and consult people who are going in the same direction or have already reached your destination. One consultation might not be enough. What grades should you aim for? What exams do you need to pass? Who do you need to speak with to expand your network?

Tackle goal setting with perseverance. It's not a one-time activity, but a regular commitment. I never set an end-point that removes the need for this exercise. I just have goals for what I want to do next. Once I conquer them, I set new goals.

Making Your Goals Realistic

Setting aside time to research and internalise your goals allows you to see them in the context of your present reality. There's nothing wrong with dreaming big; the problem lies in the fact that dreams don't cancel the truth about your current situation.

You have to acknowledge weaknesses that you have to work on first or restrictions you need to overcome. Is it finances? Other obligations? Perhaps it's a mentality that keeps you from getting along with patients or accepting criticism from others or your mentors.

Incorporate the solutions in your goal setting. Refusing to address these issues will impede your growth and stifle the opportunities that come your way. This part of your journey will develop the qualities you need to win your next challenge. Now is the time to step up and tap the limitless potential inside of you.

Mac Anderson said, 'Dream big dreams, but never forget that realistic short-term goals are the keys to your success.'

Keep Your Eyes on the Big Picture But Focus on Your Immediate Goals

Visualisation plays a major role in my life. I visualise my goals and who I need to become to reach them. Doing so enables me to live as if I am already that person, and that positions me to act with the confidence I need to accomplish the success I strive for.

I also visualise smaller tasks, such as procedures I am about to perform (more on that in the succeeding chapters).

It is possible to get so caught up in the future that you forget to focus on your goals. It's like driving in the night from London to Birmingham. You turn on your car lights to illuminate the first ten meters, and once you've crossed that, you will see the next ten meters. Keep doing this, and before you know it, you would have covered the entire hundred miles to Birmingham. Focus on the goals that will lead you to your destination. Focusing on the destination can become overwhelming.

The effort you put in on a daily and weekly basis is essential to accomplishing the goals that will materialise your vision. These are the ten metres ahead of you that you need to cover before doing the next ten metres. Without giving your full attention to the tasks that need doing *right now*, there is little chance that you will get far.

Steve Jobs made a powerful point about focus when he said, 'People think focus means saying yes to the thing you've got to focus on. But that's not what it means at all. It means saying no to the hundred other good ideas that there are.'

It's impossible to focus when you have allowed yourself to be pulled in a dozen different directions. Choosing a path and setting goals are not enough to drive your focus. It's about being intentional in everything you do, deciding daily to invest your time, money, and effort on things that contribute to the big picture.

I was overweight growing up and people teased me because of it. They came up with the most obnoxious names for me, and I would be lying if I say it never bothered me. This struggle continued into my first year in university. There was a moment when it just dawned on me that I have excelled in everything else, but I have let myself fail in this department. I had enough, and I decided to fix my situation.

With the help of a coach, I exerted all my physical and mental prowess into getting fit. I set my mind to losing weight that summer no matter what it took.

I remember the shocked expressions of my classmates outside the lecture theatre at the beginning of the new academic year. My efforts had paid off and everybody saw it.

I didn't just say yes to running five times a week that summer. I had to say dozens of no's to food I should not eat, an extended rest day I should not take, and thoughts I should not tolerate. To this day, I'm conscious of my weight and do my best to maintain a healthy lifestyle. This means regularly saying yes to the right things and no to temptations.

I do that by keeping in mind the big picture—which is staying in shape—and focusing on my daily goal—which is choosing healthy alternatives and portions.

The same principles apply to your studies, work, and personal life. What have you been saying yes to that is taking too much of your time and attention? What opportunities have you been saying no to?

It only looks more complex than it actually is because many people fear confronting their weaknesses and mistakes. Without this confrontation, though, you cannot commit to the actions that will help you reach your goals. Name these shortcomings and make a list. It's easier to act on them when you know exactly what they are.

When you are intentional with the details of your life, you can focus in the moment, and each focused moment is an investment towards your future.

Goals Change—That's OK

Sometimes, there's more than one road to get to the same destination. This is why visualisation is important to me. It reminds me of what I envisage for myself in the future because the goals I set or the things I say yes to-like the first partnership-might lead to a dead end.

After that partnership, I drafted new goals, which flew me to Brazil, South Africa, and many other countries. I tapped the experiences of experts and learnt implant dentistry.

When you have poured your hopes and skills towards a road that is suddenly cut short, your vision will pick you up and set you in another path. Rest and re-evaluate if you have to. Stay awake in the middle of the night visualizing again the person you want to be.

It's a cycle of checking, taking a course of action, and re-checking. Conjure a vision, set the next goal, focus all your effort and energy into that, visualise, execute, and repeat.

Zig Ziglar said, 'When obstacles arise you change your direction to achieve your goals, you do not change your decision to get there.'

Remember that it is not the end of your dreams when your plans derail. The fact is, if you do enough of anything, you are bound to make mistakes. That's okay. It is simply part of the learning process, and your job is to pick up as many lessons as you can from them.

Focus on the next thing but keep in mind the direction in which you are going.

Chapter 2

Plan Ahead and Practice Mental Rehearsal

'All things are created twice: first mentally, then physically. The key to creativity is to begin with the end in mind, with a vision, a blueprint.'

Stephen Covey

I recently gave a lecture on the five keys to surgical mastery which summarises the keys to successful practices in surgery.

It starts with setting the right environment, equipment, and staff support. These three elements are the ones that make any surgical procedure possible.

The next is to visualise the procedure before you do it. Remember that all things are created twice: first mentally, and then physically.

Whenever you perform any surgery, it is crucial to spend time visualising it from start to finish before you do it. Some treatments are more complicated than others, thus making visualisation even more critical.

Even now, big operations make me nervous. I take this as a sign that no tenure or experience diminishes the care with which I deal with each patient.

I also believe that if I didn't feel this way, I should not be doing this work.

Each of us in this profession need to keep in mind that we bear a responsibility to our patients. The excellence of our service should exceed the amount of money we get paid for these procedures. It's their health at stake, and that's something we should never take lightly.

This is why I make mental rehearsal a part of my routine and you should, too.

The Power of the Mind

Assistant Professor of Psychology Alia Crum, PhD, of the Stanford Mind and Body Lab said 'Our minds aren't passive observers, simply perceiving reality as it is. Our minds actually change reality.'

Studies show that the mind is so powerful that our perception of pain can intensify based on our expectations, and that it can affect the recovery period. Even claims on marketing ads such as a 'hearty meal' can suffice to make you feel fuller and healthier after eating said meal.

Businessmen utilise this concept to great success, and they continue to do so now with the widespread reach of social media. They tell you what to think of an item or service they offer and, if you see or hear it long enough, you often concede to that impression.

Imagine what you can do if you harness this same power to realise your dreams.

Marisa Peer, Britain's top therapist, encourages people to collaborate with their minds and use its transformative power to inspire change.

There are four things you need to know about the mind in order to do this:

1. It will do exactly what it thinks you want to do;
2. It is wired to move you towards pleasure and away from pain;

3. It responds to words you say to yourself and images you make in your head;
4. It loves what is familiar;

Your mind always looks after your best interest. If you say that you hate waking up early to exercise and you don't want to spend the weekend studying, you are telling your mind that these activities are not good for you. This urges it to procrastinate and look for ways out of those situations.

Your mind thrives from the specificity of the language you use to communicate with it. Tell it instead that you love waking up early and spending the night studying. You choose to do these things because they are beneficial to you and that's what you want.

Collaborate with your mind to think differently about things that you would normally dread or complain about. Change your language and communicate difficult tasks as things you want to do because you like them.

We discussed in the previous chapter that in order to achieve your goals, you will have to say yes or no to certain things. You will also need to keep in mind the big picture so that you don't get lost when your goals lead to a dead end.

The key to achieving both is by being more conscious of your thought patterns and restructuring them to a design that's attractive to you. Since your mind moves away from pain and towards pleasure, thinking of activities you consider painful or difficult as something that brings you enjoyment makes a huge difference in your life.

You are the only person who can label your experiences as one or the other. Choose to label studying and hard work as pleasurable. Link half-hearted efforts and negativity to pain. As you change the way you perceive things, you will notice yourself gravitating more towards doing activities that would previously trigger procrastination.

It's easier to do this when you take full control of the images you make in your head and the words you say to yourself, which is Marisa Peer's third point. These are the two actions that impact the way you feel about anything at any given moment. Your mind will give you exactly what you ask it for. If you tell yourself that you will succeed, you will. If you tell yourself that you can't do something, you most certainly won't make it.

The thoughts and words you meditate on will inevitably determine the outcome of everything you do: every single procedure, patient interaction, and progress you make in your field.

Experts used to claim that it was impossible for the human body to run a mile in under four minutes. It's something people have been trying to achieve for years with no success. That is, until Roger Bannister rose above that belief and ran the distance in 3:59.4.

He told his mind that he wanted to overcome the four-minute barrier. He perceived the physical strain as pleasurable. He said and thought only excellent things about himself. He familiarised himself with the discipline and exertion that would lead him to his goal. When he finally made the impossible possible, he not only broke the four-minute barrier. He proved to everyone that humans are capable of achieving anything we set our minds on.

I firmly believe that the most effective way you can do this is through mental rehearsal.

What is Mental Rehearsal?

This is not the same as daydreaming. When you form images in your mind intentionally and meditate on them before a task, it's called mental rehearsal or, as some would like to put it, 'imagined practice'.

Simply telling yourself that you will accomplish a task correctly next time cannot guarantee that you will. Looking at it positively is a beginning, but you have to use the power of your imagination to picture how you will do it correctly.

While it cannot replace the fruits of physical practice, rehearsing activities in your head acts as a supplement that conditions your mind to achieve your goals.

How exactly does it do that?

From Mental to Physical

Stephen Covey authored one of the most renowned books in the field of personal development, *The 7 Habits of Highly Effective People*. In it, he said, 'All things are created twice: first mentally, then physically. The key to creativity is to begin with the end in mind, with a vision, a blueprint of the desired result.'

Mental rehearsal focuses primarily on the power of Marisa Peer's fourth point, which is making the unfamiliar familiar.

After you've told your mind exactly what you want it to do, linked it with pleasure, and given yourself the right words and images, familiarisation will set the momentum for improvement. It is the tool that will create the change first in your mind, and then in reality.

Your mind is programmed to chase what is familiar. If what is familiar to you is showing up to appointments late and putting off work until the last moment, that is what your mind will always go for. Estrange yourself from these bad habits and familiarize yourself with the work ethic and character required for success.

Nikola Tesla, inventor of the alternating-current electric system, has this to say about it: 'My method is different. I do not rush into actual work. When I get a new idea, I start at once building it up in my imagination, and make improvements and operate the device in my mind. When I have gone so far as to embody everything in my invention, every possible improvement I can think of, and when I see no fault anywhere, I put into concrete form the final product of my brain.'

He ended up patenting 300 inventions worldwide, some of them contributing to today's use of television and other electronics.

Use mental rehearsal to familiarise yourself with skills that you are developing and tasks that you want to improve on. Imagine yourself handling with composure the same circumstances that had caused you to panic in real life. Create a clear picture of yourself dealing with difficult patients with the calm and understanding of a true professional. What words will you use? What body language will convey your empathy?

You make your desired output familiar because you've practiced it a hundred times in your head.

Making the unfamiliar familiar will inevitably become the fuel that drives your actions. Your body will always follow where your mind leads, so make sure that you are leading it through the right means and in the right direction.

Over time, these things will become part of your subconscious mind, which makes them a natural component of your emotional, mental, and physical response. It's like driving. When you have travelled the same road many times, you can anticipate all the turns and respond to them instinctively. The procedures and the attitude become so ingrained in you that you don't even think about them anymore.

Your ability to transfer an idea from your imagination (conscious) to your beliefs (subconscious) will determine your actions and then your success. Mental rehearsal achieves this for you because when you visualise, your mind can't tell the difference between imagination and reality.

Henry Ford said, 'Whether you think you can or think you cannot, you are most certainly right.'

And because our actions like to be in agreement with our beliefs, what you visualize and repeatedly rehearse in your mind is what you will inevitably act upon.

Another way that familiarisation through mental rehearsal helps is by reducing stress and curbing negative thoughts. When you are about to do something you dread, stress and negativity increases your chances of failure. They rob you of your confidence and you set yourself up to make mistakes.

Mental rehearsal narrows your focus to only one possibility—success. This conditioning doesn't guarantee that you will not make any mistakes. Instead, it allows you to enter a task with a mindset that enables you to perform at your best.

Just like goal setting, mental rehearsal is not a one-time activity. It's a discipline—one that is paramount to our line of work.

Applying It To Your Work

Put intention and positive energy into your vision. Clarify what you want. Root out any negativity that stops you from attaining this and believe that you have the ability to create the result you desire. These are the guidelines I follow for mental rehearsal, and they are integral elements mentioned earlier about the five keys to surgical mastery.

After setting the right environment, equipment, and staff, I take the time to mentally rehearse every single step that I would take throughout a procedure, and I will repeatedly do that until I have done it correctly in my mind. Thus, when I get to performing the actual procedure, it would feel natural to me because I have already rehearsed it many times in my head.

There are times that I would even put it on paper. This is what I call "written rehearsal." I would write not only the main points, but all the steps from the system, from anaesthetic to other specifics of the entire process.

Doing so enables me to proceed to the third point, which is to overcome procrastination. Remember that the mind is powerful, and you can reverse how you perceive a task you've been dreading. Make the task attractive and the emotions that trigger procrastination will retreat.

Mental rehearsal is only beneficial if you've actually managed to perform the task.

Gene Hayden said, 'Following-through is the only thing that separates dreamers from people that accomplish great things.'

This applies not only to surgery, but to other areas of your career as well. A lot of clinicians attend courses but never put to practice what they learn. In the same way, you can visualise yourself succeeding, but only action can translate it into reality.

Commit everything you have to it and finish the race no matter what it takes. Struggle your way into achieving the objective. You didn't start it only to throw in the towel halfway through. You can say no to quitting and yes to crossing that finish line because that's what you envisioned yourself doing.

Once you are done, reward yourself. You should always be the first person to appreciate your hard work. It's your mind and body that exerted the effort, and showing gratitude to yourself is one way to take care of them.

There are other means through which you can apply mental rehearsal to your career. May it be in studying, passing a job interview, dealing with patients, managing difficult colleagues, or simply bolstering your mastery of certain skills.

Utilise this tool to your advantage. It's free, it's powerful, and the potential is in you to propel the changes that will lead to your success.

Applying It To Your Colleagues

The fourth step of the 5 keys to success in surgery mentioned earlier is to reflect on your performance. While it's essential that you make time to do this by yourself, you must also learn to do this with your team and your mentor.

You can't perform a surgery on your own. You have to function as a team, which makes it crucial to build trust and camaraderie. To do that, however, you need to open yourself to criticism, advice, and correction. Those three aren't always easy to take, but for the sake of excellence and teamwork, you have to face them.

Mental rehearsal also plays a part in enabling you to deal with these like a professional. You may have to run different scenarios in your head on how to best receive feedback. If you know you have the tendency to be upset or to react poorly to receiving advice, mental rehearsal will prepare you to be gracious and dignified regardless of what anyone says and how they say it.

Responding correctly to people is imperative to your growth and development. Not everyone is aware of the right way to give and receive feedback, that's why you have to learn to restrain your emotions and see it through an objective lens. We'll discuss this further on the chapters about communication and leadership.

Similarly, you will experience giving feedback to someone who receives it with indifference. Mental rehearsal equips you to modify your approach in a way that helps your colleague see things from your perspective.

Choosing to Believe in Yourself

The fifth and final step is to believe in yourself. You are your best partner and supporter. Cultivate in yourself a strong belief that you are capable of everything you've set your mind to achieve. It's okay to be scared and anxious from time to time - everyone feels that way, too.

Positivity turns toxic when you refuse to acknowledge that you are going through a setback and you feel the pressure. You are not a pessimist if you experience emotions other than happiness.

The positivity you want to nurture in your life is the one that meets negative emotions with compassion. It will encourage you towards a healthy means to cope and get back on your feet. Take time to consider what you can do to turn the situation around instead of punishing yourself or resorting to pretence, and ignoring the problem. Deep inside, you believe that you are worth the fight, and you will forego all hopelessness to chase your dreams.

The Dalai Lama said, 'In order to carry a positive action we must develop here a positive vision.'

Rehearse this in your mind. Visualise yourself pursuing excellence in spite of negative emotions. You have no time for self-pity and doubt, and you can help yourself act on this belief by fostering it in your imagination.

In my culture, we believe the meaning of your name is really important.

Ferhan in Arabic means "happy." I have always been a happy and positive person, and this has helped me get to where I want to be. There's also an innate desire in me to see other people happy. That's what drives me, and I believe that is what needs to drive you, too.

American businessman Harvey Mackay said, 'Positive thinking is more than just a tagline. It changes the way we behave. And I firmly believe that when I am positive, it not only makes me better, but it also makes those around me better.'

I also have faith that everything will turn out exactly as it needs to be. If something does not transpire the way I expect it to, I know it's for the best. There's a lesson in every downturn, every mistake, and every "failure."

In fact, I'm a firm believer that there is no such thing as failure, only learning. In life, we either succeed or we learn. Pick up lessons from your mistakes and take wisdom from your challenges. Make this a part of your mental rehearsal, and even the lowest point in your life will start to look to you like an opportunity to start again.

Chapter 3

Prioritise Learning Before Earning

'The best investment you can ever make is the investment in yourself as that cannot be taxed.'

Warren Buffet

I attribute my unstoppable desire for knowledge and growth to my father. My family has always put education first, and my father pushed me and my siblings to study hard. It's because of this that I always aim to broaden my knowledge, whether it's within my profession or a skill that will advance my career such as public speaking.

Learning never ends.

I'm also a strong believer that to be good at something, you have to do it every day. It's a continual effort of discovery, mastery, and rehearsal. What you learn, you engage with until you become an expert.

Once you are an expert, you maintain and develop your skills through practice, which in itself will teach you more lessons.

Every clinician should cultivate this mindset about learning. You must never stop pursuing new knowledge in every stage of your career if you are to excel and succeed.

Education is Key

When I thought about doing medicine after dentistry, I knew it would have been much simpler if I started working and making money. That's what most of my colleagues chose to do. In wanting to be different—to *stand out*—I pushed myself knowing that I will reap bigger rewards later.

The night shifts and on-calls during weekends were tough. I remember almost falling asleep on the wheel trying to get myself through medical school. Apart from the physical strain, there's also the financial burden of paying for my education and mortgage.

I had to ask my younger brother to help me with money. At the same time, I looked for work anywhere possible, from hospitals in Scotland to North West England. I would be in university during the day and in the hospital at night. I remember doing a 48-hour on-call in the east of Scotland and then traveling down to Liverpool for 9-10 a.m. starts. It wasn't easy, but I knew the pain was temporary. In comparison to the size of the reward, the hardships I had to endure seemed small.

Warren Buffet said, 'The best investment you can ever make is the investment in yourself as that cannot be taxed.'

I viewed education as an investment in myself when I pursued medicine after achieving my degree in dentistry. It was by going back to university that I expanded my mind's horizon and opened doors of opportunities that would've otherwise stayed shut.

There was more to learn, and I was determined to give my all to learn them. Putting my resolve to the test and pushing myself was painful at times, but those were the things I had to do to succeed.

People say I'm crazy for spending a further four years at university. Crazy in a good way. I voluntarily signed up to be in a room full of medical students in their early twenties, all of them just starting out. My professor was just as shocked as they were to know that I was already a qualified dentist.

This would have bothered a lot of people, but to tell you the truth, it never bothered me. They say it's a lot of effort. To me, it's completely normal.

Back in my school days, I aimed to be among the top students in my class. I enjoyed school thoroughly, and I remember being liked by my teachers. The thought of having to take a day off was unbearable.

My father would always ask me if I got the top marks, and although I wasn't first in class all the time, it conditioned me to do better.

I aimed to be in the top five percent, and Alibaba's owner, Jack Ma, shared wisdom about this when he said, 'I told my son: you don't need to be in the top three in your class, being in the middle is fine, so long as your grades aren't too bad. Only this kind of person has enough free time to learn other skills.'

Pursuing education can be challenging physically, mentally, and financially, but I overcame all of those by focusing on this principle: my success doesn't depend on other people, but on my desire, determination, and passion for attaining it.

The same applies to you.

You have to be the hardest worker in the room. Train hard, study hard, and practice even harder. That's the mentality of the people who have made history.

Kobe Bryant, one of the most renowned athletes of our time, worked out and practised shooting hoops before his fellow NBA players were even awake. People he had worked with vouched for his intense drive not only to stay in shape, but to reach the peak of his abilities. He had no excuses to pull him down, and you shouldn't harbour any in your mind either.

In life, we either have results or we have excuses. It's your choice.

Open yourself to New Information

Education doesn't stop when you graduate from an official educational institution. It stops when you ignore every opportunity afterwards to grow as a professional and as a person.

Kirk Douglas said, 'The learning process continues until the day you die.'

You always need to aim for new knowledge. If you want to succeed, you have to keep growing and seeking to be educated through whatever means possible.

Reading books is among the cheapest and most underrated ways to do this. The majority of people read one book a year on average, and I didn't want to be part of this statistic. One of the biggest changes I made was to delete my online music subscription and swap it to an audiobook subscription app. I listen to books on personal development, as well as leadership, business, and a variety of other topics that I find helpful.

I was recently listening to *Principles* by Ray Dalio, a billionaire investor and philanthropist. He discusses the nature of struggles and how we grow through them like a weightlifter would. You will feel the pain as you work towards your goal, but as you keep going at it, your muscles grow, and then you are better able to handle the weight. The same can be said in respect to personal growth.

Identify areas in your life or your profession that you need to develop and read on those subject matters. Listen to audio books, podcasts, and attend seminars that enrich your knowledge in those areas. I recommend not just books on dentistry, but also those that tackle leadership, business, finance, and personal development.

It's important for you to *make* time - not *find* time - for learning. This could mean disciplining yourself to watch less TV or to skip your usual Friday night out. Instead of listening to music on your way to work, play an audio book or a podcast. Carry a book around with you always and make it a hobby to open it while queuing for something instead of mindlessly scrolling through your social media apps.

You have enough time in a day to invest in your education. Use mental rehearsal to unlearn bad habits and to familiarise yourself with activities that benefit you. Tell your mind that you want to read, and you want to learn more. Think of it as pleasurable and believe you can develop habits that will lead to your growth.

Make self-reflection a part of your everyday routine because there's always something to learn at work. There's a lesson that comes with every patient you treat, especially the difficult ones. You can pause to examine how you could have done a procedure better. The chance to learn is everywhere—we simply need to be vigilant enough to find it.

Today, I feel like I am being led on this path automatically. Like on a conveyor belt. My environment forces me to learn. I follow the steps my environment lays out for me. Learning has become a part of my system, and it guides me to where I need to be.

Surround Yourself with Learners

Your environment will always influence your decisions. This is why it's integral that you select settings and people who will inspire you to keep learning.

A well-known quote from Jim Rohn is that 'You are the average of the five people you spend the most time with.'

Who are those five people in your life? Do they motivate you to accomplish more, or do they tempt you to be complacent? Ask yourself if you need to find a new social and professional circle that will benefit your dreams. You may not have total control over your environment all the time, but you can make decisions that bring you closer to the right people.

These people are the like-minded individuals who share similar passions and goals. They are interested in advancing their education and using their careers to help others. It's even better if these individuals are ahead of you in many ways because that will challenge you to reach their level.

I was in an environment that influenced me to go down the medical route. I worked in an oral maxillofacial surgery department where everyone was dual qualified. To be a maxillofacial surgeon, you need to be dual trained in dentistry and medicine. So that inspired me to be dual qualified as well.

Another reason to aim for such a circle a few steps ahead of you is because they are the individuals you can work with to get to your destination faster.

A colleague of mine went with me to Brazil to learn zygomatic implant surgery, and when we returned home, we treated cases together. Our strengths and insights combined fast-tracked our development.

Wilfred Peterson said, 'Walk with the dreamers, the believers, the courageous, the cheerful, the planners, the doers, the successful people with their heads in the clouds and their feet on the ground.'

You don't have to do it alone. If you are missing these people in your life, look for them. These are the relationships that will keep you in line with your goals and drive you to go beyond your limitations.

Open Yourself to Correction

I often work seven days a week and travel around the UK to collaborate with other clinicians. It's a good way for me to expose myself to an extensive network of colleagues and mentors who will not only teach me but correct me as well.

Many people nowadays don't want to receive corrections. Those who claim they do are afraid of being offended. They prioritise their emotions, and when their egos get hurt, the chance of learning is abandoned.

Learning starts when you accept that you will make mistakes at work and you will encounter people who contradict your opinions. These are normal occurrences in any profession, and by no means do they disqualify you from being competent. In fact, it's through correction that you grow to your full potential.

Ralph Waldo Emerson said, 'Let me never fall into the vulgar mistake of dreaming that I am persecuted whenever I am contradicted.'

Unlearn the mindset that people are against you if they disagree with you. If you have ever been hurt by a correction made to you in the past, then your mind will continually associate the experience with pain. Your initial response will be to avoid it.

Teach yourself to want correction and to be attracted to the notion of improving because of it. Mentally rehearse how you would respond to your mentor and colleagues. If your usual response is to walk away or to take it personally, then imagine yourself calm enough to understand what they are trying to teach. Only then will you rise above your emotions and benefit from the correction.

Double-Check Information and Advice

Does the above mean you should take everything at face value?

By all means, accept people's feedback, correction, or opinion like a professional, but do your own research. Do not take someone else's word for a fact just because they are an authority. When you are given new information, read up on the subject. Look for credible sources that can give you further knowledge about the subject matter. This is paramount in an age where anyone can publish unverified material and speculations online without repercussions.

Researching prevents you from falling victim to those and allows you to fully grasp the correction or advice you were given.

I've had several encounters with people who made claims that were not true. They don't always do it intentionally. Sometimes, it's the result of their own complacency that gets them involved in spreading misinformation. It's like Chinese whispers; what starts out as a fact gets misunderstood, and the compromised information gets passed around.

Make investigation a part of your learning method. A passive attitude towards learning will inevitably cause you to believe anything anyone says so long as it is said with conviction.

Discover Your Learning Style

Every person has a different way of learning.

Howard Gardner's *Theory of Intelligences* inspired eight learning styles that can help you determine the best approach for you.

- Visual (spatial)
- Aural (auditory)

- Verbal (linguistic)
- Physical (kinaesthetic)
- Logical (mathematical)
- Social (interpersonal)
- Solitary (intrapersonal)
- Naturalistic

A method that works for your mentor might not work for you. If you so happen to be a visual learner, copying your colleague's habit of listening to music while reading will not help you. In the same way, joining a highly recommended study group won't benefit you much if you process information best in a quiet environment.

I discovered that I learn better through watching videos and by talking about them. Drawing, writing, and visualising things also helps me in retaining knowledge.

Discover which methods work for you and stick to them. It will simplify your approach to education and hasten your growth.

Practice What You Learn

Practice is how you create things in the physical. What you start in the mind through learning, you turn into reality through relentless application. Doing it once is not enough. To be good at something, you have to practice it relentlessly every day.

I travel all over the UK to work with different clinicians. This gives me the opportunity to learn from a variety of clinicians all the time, and it has been a part of my on-going routine for a while now.

Consider taking opportunities outside of your regular work. Search for programs that give you access to respected authorities in your field and learn how they perform their tasks.

One of the ways we improve is by looking at other people and what they do. I take every chance I get to reach out to people I look up to and ask to shadow them. This way, I can observe them and try to use their methods in my own practice. The more exposure you get, the sooner you will master your specialty.

Maybe what you need to focus on is an underdeveloped skill. Find workshops and seminars you can enrol in. If it's personal development you need to work on, perform your exercises again once you are home. Stand in front of your mirror and practice your walk, hand gestures, and manner of speech. Roll your shoulders back and stand tall. Incorporate these activities to your daily routine because it's only by repeating these over and over will they become a natural part of you.

Share Your Knowledge

I aim to become better at what I do so I can help more people. My love and passion for my job spurs in me the desire to support others in their own race. The time I spend helping them boosts their growth as well as mine.

At the time of writing this book, I am doing a lot of teaching. I have been going live on social media to share my knowledge about implant dentistry.

Louis L'Amour said, 'Knowledge is like money: to be of value it must circulate, and in circulating it can increase in quantity and, hopefully, in value.'

When you get involved in teaching as a clinician, it forces you to improve your knowledge around the subject even more because you want to come across as an authoritative figure.

As for me, I take the time to study the topic I will talk about so I can relay information in a way that my audience will have no difficulty grasping. It also challenges me to do more research and achieve a level of understanding that is higher than a student would usually strive for.

There's a lot of pressure going into this, but you can use that pressure as the driving force for you to master the topic. Even then you will encounter difficult situations that you will have no other way to manage but through humility. As a mentor and a teacher, you will be asked challenging questions, and it's important that you are not ashamed to say, 'I'm not sure of the answer to that question, but let me find out and get back to you.'

There's no such thing as a perfect educator, mentor, or coach, so don't aim to be one. Choose instead to become an authority they can respect because you are sincere in your efforts to give all that you have for the sake of their progress.

I encourage all clinicians to involve themselves in teaching to some degree. This is our way of ensuring that the next generation of clinicians will learn not only the technicalities, but also the vital lessons that will lead to the betterment of our profession and the people we serve.

Finish What You Start

Last but not least, when I start something, I finish it. I don't like unaccomplished tasks.

When I finished medical school, I applied for a post as a junior doctor. It was a two-year post. Although technically, I only needed one year to complete my registration, I finished the two years. In that time, opportunities opened for me that I would've missed had I not stayed for the duration of my post.

Darren Hardy said, 'Starting is not most people's problem, staying, continuing and finishing is.'

Stick with your commitments, even if the going gets hard. Expect that you will encounter challenges, whether it is getting another degree, or simply reading a four-hundred-page book about the field you are specialising in. There will be times when you will get discouraged and you will want to quit.

Don't.

Quitting is an attitude that, when you tolerate once, you can tolerate over and over again. By the time you realize how many commitments you have left behind, you have already drifted so far from your dreams that it has become a vague picture in the horizon of your mind.

Always finish what you start, no matter how big or small. The more you do it, the more naturally it will come to you to see every task, goal, and dream to its completion.

Over time, you will build the confidence you need to be bolder and more persistent in achieving your dreams.

Chapter 4

Confidence and Self-Belief

'Whatever we expect with confidence becomes our own self-fulfilling prophecy.'

Brian Tracey

Another reason I pursued medicine is because I wanted to become an oral and maxillofacial surgeon. It's a speciality that excited me and in order to pursue it, I had to attain degrees in dentistry and medicine.

Apart from the many challenges I mentioned in the previous chapter about this season in my life, I also faced debts after finishing this degree.

I was behind all my peers financially. They had chosen to earn money first, and my situation looked like it would have benefited from that decision, too.

What kept me moving forward in spite of that is the confidence that I was capable of achieving what I set out to do. The road I chose for myself was different, and it mattered that I believed in myself first before anybody else did.

When you are doing what you are meant to do, you have to accept that not everyone will understand and support you. That's okay. That's normal.

Golda Meir said, 'Trust yourself. Create the kind of self that you will be happy to live with all your life. Make the most of yourself by fanning the tiny, inner sparks of possibility into flames of achievement.'

It's your thoughts and opinions towards yourself that you should care about most because those are the ones that impact your success. Trust yourself and cultivate a self-belief that will lift your perspective above all doubt and hardships.

Today, I am financially secure; and this has allowed me to be generous with my money, time, and skills.

Building Your Confidence

Among all other things that can keep you from achieving success, it's a lack of confidence that will pull you down the fastest. If you are suffering from a shortage or lack of it altogether, you need to work on the beliefs that are causing you to doubt yourself.

Your past experiences play a huge role in this. Perhaps you tried something new and failed, or your best efforts ended up causing you embarrassment. The pain linked to those memories hinder you from stepping out of your comfort zone today because you are afraid of reliving those discomforts.

The first thing you need to do is to stop it. Cut short any trip down memory lane that magnifies those bad experiences. Talk about them with someone who can help you process those experiences. It's through this that you will get a fresh perspective about what you initially labelled as an embarrassment or a failure.

From there, tell your mind that you want to leave your comfort zone again and that it's desirable. Condition your mind to perceive risks as pleasurable, and you will slowly untangle yourself from doubt.

Build yourself up with positive words and images daily. Remember that self-belief is about the words you say to yourself. Confidence is about the image you have of yourself. You cannot say that you are confident if you paint pictures of defeat all the time.

Mentally rehearse the big and small leaps you are taking towards your dreams and turn them into reality. It's by actually moving your feet outside the perimeter of your comfort zone that you begin to live with confidence.

Dale Carnegie said, 'Inaction breeds doubt and fear. Action breeds confidence and courage. If you want to conquer fear, do not sit home and think about it. Go out and get busy.'

A lot of dentists complete courses, yet they still do not have the confidence to practice what they learned.

Once you have gone through the appropriate training, read the books, and completed the courses, you have to believe in yourself and commit to the daily application of the knowledge and skills you acquired.

Mohammad Ali believed he was the greatest before the world acknowledged it. He trained hard, of course, but he also had unstoppable self-belief.

So, the next time you tell yourself that you can't do this or that, stop and think if you are showing the confidence you need to succeed. Anytime the answer is no, you have to work on increasing your confidence.

Handling the Opinion of Others

Sometimes people will talk down to you. It is common when you are working in big teams composed of a variety of people. Not everyone will show you the respect you deserve, and you have to decide how to handle that.

Will you succumb to self-doubt, or will your confidence push through to help you perform at your best?

Jean Sibelius said, 'If you really put a small value upon yourself, rest assured that the world will not raise your price. Pay no attention to what the critics say. A statue has never been erected in honour of a critic.'

I found myself in this situation before, and if you have ever been a junior doctor, you will be familiar with my story.

Everyone likes to believe that junior doctors know nothing. It is a stigma that comes with the position, and it could have caused people to treat me poorly.

However, that never happened to me. I believe it's because I showed the kind of confidence that warranted people's respect. I knew how hard I studied and worked on my skills. I entered that post certain that I was capable of excelling in all the tasks they expected me to perform.

My resolve to believe in myself led others to believe in me.

Arthur Ashe said, 'One important key to success is self-confidence. An important key to self-confidence is preparation.'

The early years as a doctor and working in your foundation years is very challenging. Many struggle to survive this environment. Within days of being on the job, you may start feeling out of your depth, and the temptation to quit will be at its strongest.

For me it wasn't a problem, and it should not have to be for you either.

You have to go to school or to work with a mindset that deflects people's biases, negativity, and criticism. It's by preparing yourself to meet opposition that you take charge of your response, and therefore the outcome.

There will always be people who are not supportive of you. Again, that's normal, and by all means, expect it in every area of your life. Focus instead on what you can control, and how you view yourself in spite of it.

I think my resourcefulness and belief comes from the fact I've lasted several night shifts alone, and that forced me to work out things by myself.

I thought to myself that if people before me managed, so can I.

If someone else can do it, so can I.

If they can survive the harsh environment, then I can survive it as well.

Lao Tzu said, 'Because one believes in oneself, one doesn't try to convince others. Because one is content with oneself, one doesn't need others' approval. Because one accepts oneself, the whole world accepts him or her.'

If there is anything I believe in enough and I'm driven by the desire to do it, I will go after it with all my might regardless of what others say to stop me.

The Role of Humility

Confidence in yourself is also related to humility. If you start thinking you are doing better than others, you are going backwards.

Self-belief and confidence shouldn't be boastful. There's always the danger of building up those two traits and inflating your ego in the process. Be vigilant so as to avoid mistaking one for the other, because the only thing worse than lacking self-confidence is living with a contorted understanding of it.

Carl Gustav Jung said, 'Through pride we are ever deceiving ourselves. But deep down below the surface of the average conscience a still, small voice says to us, something is out of tune.'

You may want to be an authority in your area of expertise, but you won't make the impact you wish to make if your confidence is rooted in arrogance.

Pride destroys true greatness, but humility magnifies it.

Humility is not weakness. It's a mindset that's been liberated from pride and arrogance. When you are humble, you are more open to learn, improve, make new associations, and appreciate the success of those around you.

My focus is never on the money I'm going to make with each endeavour, but on the learning. I'm convinced that even when I'm mentoring, it presents an opportunity for me to learn as well. It matters to me that I build a relationship and share the notion that even though we're at different points in our career, we can both be excited about getting better.

When I develop this mindset towards everything I do and everyone I encounter, it reinforces my humility. I become so secure about who I am and what I'm worth that I'm not moved by everybody else's attempt to prove they are better.

Humility reminds me that I don't need to please the crowd. It gives me the understanding that I am a work-in-progress, but that I am progressing.

When your confidence and self-belief grows simultaneously with your humility, it's easier to take criticism in your stride, because you know that your confidence doesn't come from showing everyone that you know it all and can do it all.

It also keeps you in check, because it is important in our profession to put our patients first, to know that we are striving for improvement so they may benefit from it.

People who spend time with me know I love my work. I love helping people. I give my patients not just a new smile—I give them their confidence back.

When patients are grateful for my services, there is nothing more I could possibly wish for. It makes me feel like all the hard work and challenges I've been through are paying off.

It's only through humility that you develop a heart of service and appreciate the positive impact you leave in other people's lives.

Choose Who You Listen To

You can't stop people from giving you unsolicited advice or feedback. Everyone has their own opinion, and most feel that they are doing you a favour by sharing them.

It's crucial in building your self-confidence that you decide not to take everybody's words to heart. If you do, you will be left trying to please every single person around you and achieving nothing.

Intention is what differentiates a critic from a friend. I won't mull over a stranger's remark, but I will pause to evaluate my actions if the same remark comes from someone I value and who values me back. This is because I'm sure this person wouldn't have called me out if he or she didn't mean well.

Frank A. Clark said, 'Criticism, like rain, should be gentle enough to nourish a man's growth without destroying his roots.'

The right people will give you due support as well as criticism, and both will always nourish your growth. They are the people whose appreciation and approval amplifies your self-confidence because they share your vision. They know where you want to go and how you want to get there, and if you need an outside perspective on your progress, it's their opinion you rely on.

The most influential person in my life is my father. He always pushed me to work hard so I wouldn't have to work as a shopkeeper like he did. He sacrificed his personal desires to allow me and my siblings to have everything. We are not perfect, but two teachers, two dentists, and one lawyer are proof enough that his hard work paid off. He proudly displays all our degree certificates in the hallway at home.

My dad always found it hard to show his affection for us when we were children, so my mother made sure to fill that gap. She gave us so much love and I'm forever grateful for that.

In 2011, I met another person whose love and support mirrored that of my parents—my wife. I always assumed I would get married between the age of twenty-eight and twenty-nine, and that turned out to be the case.

The freedom of living away from my parents to get my degree in medicine led to unpredictability in my life. That made me feel the need for more stability in my life, and marriage provided that. Life was certainly calmer afterwards, but we also experienced our fair share of challenges.

Following completion of medical school, I brought my family back to Glasgow near where I grew up. It wasn't my wife's ideal scenario, seeing as she is from West Yorkshire. Adapting was difficult for her, but since having children, she's relaxed and settled in Scotland now.

The two of us have strong personalities and we're both quite opinionated. But whatever differences we have don't change the fact that I would not be where I am now without her support and dedication to our family. She stays at home while I travel around the country and further afield. It's with her blessing that I continue to be relentless in chasing my goals.

I met some of my mentors and most cherished friends during this phase. They played a huge part in propelling me forward, and I'll discuss more about them in the chapter about mentorship.

These are some of the people whose feedback I take very seriously. They are not just passers-by or observers in my life; they are contributors to my dreams and identity.

Name the people in your life whose opinions you will pay attention to. It's better to listen to a few and grow than to listen to everybody and lose yourself in the process.

You Are Your Greatest Partner - And Competition

You are the only person who can truly limit yourself. You will feel discomfort and commit mistakes. How that affects your self-confidence is your decision to make.

You are competing with nobody else, but at the same time you are your greatest partner. It's your records and achievements that you have to break, but it's also through your own resolve that you will break them. Collaborate with your mind. Self-confidence begins and ends with you.

William Hazlitt said, 'As is our confidence, so is our capacity.'

Does possessing self-confidence mean that you will never feel scared? Not at all.

You must accept that fear, mistakes, and discomfort don't signal the end of your dreams. In fact, they are evidence that you are taking enough action towards your dreams to attract opposition.

You also edge closer to things that bring you discomfort as you grow into the person you want to become.

I used to be shy and I had to overcome that because I knew it would hinder me from going places and meeting new people. Doing this was especially important in attaining my goals because I had to constantly put myself out there.

A specific discomfort I had to conquer was promoting myself on social media. I needed to create content and establish an online platform. Did I wait until I felt at ease before doing it? No. If I had waited, I wouldn't get anywhere, so I did it in spite of my discomfort.

At some point in your journey, you will have to be comfortable with the feeling of being uncomfortable.

I developed this mindset because one of my aims is to talk in front of thousands of people. My vision involves reaching crowds of clinicians, and then expanding to other professions. It could be through television, radio, or other public speaking opportunities. Right now, I'm more active in webinars, and I invest in that because it will help me build the confidence to switch to a bigger, bolder platform.

This desire stems from my belief that I can bring value. The more exposure I get, the more people I can help. It's not about the money or the recognition, but about fulfilling my purpose.

So, whenever I have to do something new, I tell myself to feel the fear and do it anyway.

You can avoid mistakes, but they will always happen one way or another if you do enough of anything. They are part of the journey, and I have begun to consider them as stepping stones to my success.

Stand tall. Chest out.

It is important as clinicians that we are aware of our value. We are not simply checking, cleaning, and fixing teeth.

We serve people and offer solutions that restore their quality of life. The power of a smile should never be underestimated. Allowing patients to smile with confidence is a priceless gift. Remember that you are making a difference. Use it to deepen the roots of your confidence.

Chapter 5

Overcoming Challenges and Complications

'We need to accept that we won't always make the right decisions, that we'll screw up royally sometimes-understanding that failure is not the opposite of success, it's part of success.'

Arianna Huffington

There's a good reason a lot of people don't like tests. There's no clearer indicator of failure and success than taking one. A good example is a driving test, which I failed three times.

By my fourth attempt, I passed.

It's a simple scenario that you can probably relate to and a powerful example of how we must deal with failure. We keep on trying because with each new effort we exert, we come closer to getting it right.

Sadly, not everyone shares this mindset. Some people try only once or twice before allowing the debilitating feeling of failure hold them back.

These feelings don't come out of nowhere. It stems from past experiences that have shaped your perspective of failure, and that's what's stopping you from trying again.

Our memories from one to seven years old shape us the most. If you were criticized or humiliated, you may have developed a paralyzing view of failure. It's at this point that you have unconsciously taught your brain to steer clear of it and avoid the pain, hence any present distaste for anything that could even remotely give you a similar experience.

Fearing and avoiding failure has become instinctual. Your brain thinks it's protecting you from dangerous situations, and while it succeeds in guarding your emotions, it also hinders you from achieving your goals.

If you are to develop the mindset of a great clinician, you have to understand that there's more to failure than you have led yourself to believe. Yes, nobody wants to fail, but that doesn't change the fact that it'll be a regular companion of yours as you walk the road to success.

If you are to change your mindset about it, the first thing you have to do is to redefine failure.

Changing Your Mindset About Failure

On the exact days I failed my first, second, and third driving tests, I would have classified those experiences as failures. But moving forward to my fourth attempt, I acknowledged that it was through the first few tries that I learned where I went wrong and what to improve on.

After getting my license, do I still call all my previous attempts "failures," or merely steppingstones to my success?

Winston Churchill said, 'Success is not final, failure is not final, it is the courage to continue that counts.'

We can't be quick to classify events as failures. If I had done that, I wouldn't be an implant dentist today.

I enjoyed my time as a medical doctor but realized soon enough that a career in maxillofacial surgery was not what I wanted in my life.

Yes, as a maxfax surgeon I would be carrying out exciting surgeries working in a hospital and be part of a big team. I would be well respected in this field, but ultimately, I felt I would not be in control of my destiny. This resulted in my decision to complete two years of medicine and then return to dentistry.

I was lucky I had options. I entered a partnership which involved my younger brother who is also a dentist and a number of other people. We invested in buying and building seven dental practices, which grew quickly within a span of eighteen months. This great start gave us hope for a promising future, but the partnership soon failed.

Like I mentioned in a previous chapter, I bounced back from this by pursuing implant dentistry. Although that time in my career was difficult, I decided that the only way this will become a failure is if I don't move forward and use this experience to lead me somewhere better.

Arianna Huffington said, 'We need to accept that we won't always make the right decisions, that we'll screw up royally sometimes—understanding that failure is not the opposite of success, it's part of success.'

You make it a part of your success when you pick yourself up again and use your experiences to improve. There are a lot of things in life that we label as failure prematurely. It's as though we only get one shot at everything, when in fact a lot of things we aim for appear far from our reach only when we stop reaching for them.

Respond to these events in a way that transforms them into stepping stones for your success. In order for you to achieve that, you need to develop your problem-solving skills.

Complications Will Arise - Prepare for Them

Clinicians can't avoid complications. They are part of our profession, and once you are faced with one, you have to know how to respond to them.

Forming the proper response always starts in your mind. In the same way that you can bolster your confidence by utilizing the four main points Marisa Peer taught, you can condition yourself to respond - not react - to complications.

Most people's initial response to them is to dwell on the results or on the on-going dilemma. While it's vital that you examine your actions, your focus should be on the possible solutions you can apply.

How can you solve this problem? What new approaches can you make towards the predicament?

With the right mental reinforcement, this line of thinking will become your instinctual attitude towards any complication.

Just recently, I was mentoring a colleague in full arch implants and I misplaced an implant into the maxillary sinus. This is a complication that can happen, but it was the first time it happened to me. Poor planning and overconfidence resulted in this complication.

My response was to stay calm and manage the situation. I accessed the maxillary sinus through a lateral window and removed the implant. We continued with the rest of the surgery and the outcome was successful.

The complication could have caused me to feel bad about my overconfidence, but I set it aside in favour of finding a solution. There was time for self-reflection later. At that moment, what mattered was that I solved the problem.

Problem-solving skills, however, aren't developed overnight. Just like any skill, you hone them with continual practice until they become a natural part of you. The goal is for you to reach a point wherein you don't even think about what direction to take. Your mindset automatically moves you towards finding solutions.

Develop Your Problem-Solving Skills

Excellent problem-solving skills are crucial to become competent in surgery. This includes your ability to recognize a problem and identify its cause. Then manage it.

When something goes wrong, your instinct may be to panic. Adrenaline takes over, which can spur you into action, but it may also cloud your judgment.

Panic causes us to blow small complications out of proportion. This emotional response may transform a little glitch into a massive crisis in your mind. Take a deep breath, evaluate, and then act. It is important to act swiftly, but never rush. The difference between the two is that the former is often performed with intention, while the latter, with recklessness.

Remaining calm is instrumental in successfully managing unexpected situations.

This is where mental rehearsal comes in handy before procedures. By picturing every step and every action, you will begin to familiarise yourself with your ideal performance. These mental rehearsals sink into your subconscious, and with enough practice, they can lead your hands automatically.

Visualise potential problems that can arise and solutions you can pursue. It's helpful to prioritise the more common events instead of going through every single thing that can go wrong. Not only will that frustrate you, but it can also affect your confidence.

Go through the usual complications linked to a procedure, and bear in mind that at the core of good problem-solving skills is critical thinking.

Critical thinking is the process of carefully and systematically analysing problems to find ways to solve them. It involves identifying several possible solutions and then logically evaluating each one, comparing them to one another on their merits, and then selecting the one that you conclude is the most promising.

It's vital that you get the input of your team and the other people who are immediately involved in the complication. Be calm enough to remain receptive to their insight and confident enough also to proceed with the best course of action.

Through this, your problem-solving skills will develop over time, and you will slowly find it easier to manage complications as you go along.

Micro & Macro Failures

Failures can be split into two categories: micro and macro.

Micro is the small day-to-day mishaps you experience. It's possible to get so caught up in these that your focus derails. You may ponder over the disappointment for too long and you end up generalising the failure because you are overcome by emotions.

This leaves you feeling like you have done nothing right. You could overlook everything else you did correctly because you have chosen to amplify the micro failure.

I failed the entrance exam to secondary school on two occasions. The third time I applied, they just let me in, and only because they had an open slot, and my dad was willing to pay the school fees.

I could have generalised my feelings of disappointment to the point of associating it with my identity, but I didn't. It was not a pleasant experience, but I've set my eyes on the big picture, and that involved believing in what I was capable of achieving in spite of my setbacks.

Getting my driver's license is another example that proved helpful in shifting my perspective towards failure. I used what I learnt from my three attempts to motivate me when I faced bigger problems in life.

I told myself that if I kept on learning from my previous experiences, I would end up with all the knowledge and skills I needed to make my next attempt successful.

Solve the small things and use them to develop the resilience that will help you overcome the macro failures.

The macro failures of your life will feel more glaring and difficult to get back up from. But because you've used the micro failures to sharpen your new perspective on failure, you are better equipped to use your problem-solving skills on the more daunting circumstances you will face.

My partnership that ended is an example of a macro failure. It was a big enough endeavour to have influenced the direction I was taking, and it did, but not in the way I expected it to. Instead of paving the way to obtaining more clinics, it closed the doors that would lead to such outcomes. I then shifted my focus to another opportunity open to me - implant dentistry.

If I had not managed my response to the day-to-day failures, I would've developed a fixed mindset that made the end of the partnership seem like a devastating loss.

This goes to show that there's opportunity in every failure.

You will never reach a point of perfection, no matter how long or well you've been doing these things. Your primary motivation must be to grow and develop as a clinician, both for your benefit and for others.

Assuming Responsibility

Perhaps the only thing more difficult than failing is having to assume responsibility for that failure. It's like admitting that you weren't good enough, and that's hard for a clinician to swallow.

The mentality of 'not being good enough', however, is as debilitating as it is inaccurate. When you think that way because you failed at something, you link your identity to the mistake. You forget that you can correct mistakes, and there's room for improvement.

Assuming responsibility, therefore, should be more a matter of where you can improve rather than where you had gone wrong. In order for you to move forward, you have to first acknowledge the skills you have to develop and the attitude you need to change. You admit your shortcomings and take it upon yourself to address them.

You need to find a balance between taking responsibility for a failure and not being too harsh on yourself for it.

Jim Rohn said, 'Don't wish it were easier, wish you were better.'

Overcoming challenges and obstacles is what makes life meaningful. I hope your dreams and visions are big enough to be difficult.

When superman was first developed as a comic book character, he was so strong and powerful that he overcame all obstacles easily. There were no doubts in the readers' minds that he'd win no matter what he faced. It was only when the authors made him weaker that the stories became interesting.

It is not the easy path that makes for a meaningful life - it is the hard path, and becoming a better, stronger, more resilient, and more resourceful person is what gives significance to your story.

So, when you make a mistake - just like when you achieve success—take credit for it.

There should be nothing humiliating or crippling about failure as long as you use it as an opportunity to become better.

Assuming responsibility is also a sign of self-respect. The people around you, too, will likely respect you for having the boldness to admit your faults instead of pointing fingers. It's in having this kind of humility that you open yourself to learn new techniques, reach out to mentors, and achieve excellence as a clinician.

Support Network—Do You Have One?

I cannot stress enough the significance of being in the right environment and surrounding yourself with people who share your vision and your values.

These are the people who need to be part of your support network because they can provide the encouragement you need in the context of your mindset and goals. They know you well enough to identify what kind of encouragement you respond to and how they can be with you in your lowest moments.

Establish a network of clinicians around you that consist of colleagues and mentors. These are the people you can consult with to reflect following the completion of a procedure.

This support network in your workplace/ environment serves as an accessible source of encouragement through the micro and macro failures you will experience. While you are your primary supporter, it's good to receive assurance from other people that mistakes happen, and that's okay.

In the same way that they are available for you, be present for their needs as well. Make it a culture in your team to provide assistance for each other.

Create a support network outside of your work, too.

For me, it's my family, particularly my wife. We've learned so much on how to support one another through the trials of marriage and starting a family, that I know I can depend on her when the going gets tough.

There are my children who, while they are too young to give me a pep talk, provide enough encouragement just by being there.

Hana, my eldest, was born after five years of marriage. Her birth was magical as well as miraculous, because she had only one artery in her umbilical cord, when normally there should be two. The doctors were amazed that she had no abnormalities. With God's blessing, she's a healthy and active young girl, and I consider her the to be the shining star in my life always full of smiles. She just melts my heart.

My son, Adam, came as a surprise. I remember studying a course in South Africa and getting a frantic call from my wife. She was in tears when she broke the news of her latest pregnancy.

Adam was born healthy a mere fourteen months after Hana and has been another true blessing in our lives.

My wife offers me support in words and in actions, and the love I'm filled with whenever I see my young family is enough of a reason for me to keep on going in the face of any challenge.

Who supports you during tough times? Analyse your relationships and invest in those you value, and who value you back. Everyone needs a helping hand. It's crucial that you know who to reach out to when things don't go according to plan.

Chapter 6

Communication with Patients

'To effectively communicate, we must realise that we are all different in the way we perceive the world and use this understanding as a guide to our communication with others.'

Anthony Robbins

I started working in my dad's shop at nine years old. It was situated in the outskirts of Glasgow in a working-class community, and in spite of the frequent chill in the shop due to the lack of heating, I have many of fond memories working there.

People in the neighbourhood knew my father well because he had owned the shop for many years, and I was there as his little helper.

Customers often came in and noticed the little boy behind the counter, and they would strike up a conversation. What's your name? How old are you?

What school do you go to? What do you want to be when you grow up? What football team do you support?

Sometimes, they would tell my father jokingly that it's good I don't look anything like him.

I was a shy kid, but as I continued working there and engaging the customers, I learned to speak up. It soon became normal for me to talk to strangers all the time, especially during Christmas season when the shop was at its busiest.

I worked there until I was around fifteen years old, after which I landed my first official job at KFC (Kentucky Fried Chicken). Working with a team and dealing with different people wasn't new to me at that point because I'd been doing it for a long time.

I was lucky to have these experiences at an early age which improved my communication skills. Communication is the skill upon which most relationships are built and sustained.

This is especially true in our profession. It's valuable for us to know how to communicate well with our patients, colleagues, superiors, and mentees to create an environment in which everyone thrives, and our services are delivered in the highest quality.

The Importance of Good Communication Skills as a Clinician

I was not really taught much about communicating with patients during my time in dental school. It was in the years I studied medicine that I honed and refined my skills during communication classes where I would practice medical consultations with actors.

At that time, I thought that it was nonsense. Speaking to an actor? What could that accomplish? But it constituted a huge part of our yearly assessments, so I made sure to do well in it.

I realised its importance later on and how much it helped me. All of us know how to communicate, but not all of us know how to communicate well to achieve certain results.

In dentistry, we aim for specific results like getting a patient to accept treatment or to adhere to our professional advice. While our intentions are good and clear to us, poor communication skills decrease the likelihood of gaining a patient's cooperation.

They are not mind-readers; they can only respond to what you say and what you show through body language. If you use both to your advantage, they'll trust you and you can provide successful treatments.

Building trust with patients, I believe, is the most important thing.

Trust is not only integral with patients. Your communication skills will affect your relationship with everyone in your profession, especially if you are part of a bigger team in the practice. You have the administration staff, dental nursing staff, seniors, bosses, and even mentees. You need to put a lot of thought into how you are coming across in terms of words and actions.

Communication is the tool you use to build and develop a connection with people. The tricky part about this may be the fact that your approach changes depending on who is in front of you. It's unlikely that you will talk to your boss the way you talk to your colleague. The way you show respect to the former won't be exactly the same way you will show respect to the latter.

Similarly, you will want to show consideration to both mentees and patients, but the focus of one would be on learning, while the other, on trust and consent. These nuances call for the ability to know what subtle differences in tone, word choice, and body language can achieve.

After all, effective communication is not dependent on how you perceive yourself, but how the other person perceives you. That's what defines a good communicator.

The Art of Listening

Your goal must be to actively listen.

When you pay attention not only to what is being said, but also to what is being implied, you are better able to form a favourable response.

It's difficult for most people nowadays to refrain from interrupting someone while they are talking. Their focus has shifted to finding something to say, as opposed to taking the time to understand the person you are talking to.

That's not how communication should be.

Giving someone your full attention is how you discover the appropriate words and body language to use. A patient, for example, may appear bold and loud, but their stuttering and incessant foot tapping tells you that they are anxious.

This observation allows you to provide assurance, and to do so with empathy.

Active listening also shows your respect for their self-knowledge. Patients see that you are not being dismissive about their observations, and this increases the chances of coming up with a viable care plan that is accepted.

This reduces the fear in which most patients approach consultations and treatments. Addressing their emotions and attitudes towards their health removes the obstacle that keeps them from hearing their diagnoses or deciding about their care with a clear mind.

When dealing with the people you work with, you will also want to apply the same level of focus to communicate better. Circumstances can get stressful, and if you are not careful, you risk a misunderstanding that you could have avoided if only you were paying attention.

Another technique you can use is to paraphrase what has been said to you, such as when your mentor gives you instructions. Summarise what they have said to confirm that you understood everything correctly.

Ask questions when you are being briefed about a patient's history. Express verbal affirmations and non-verbal cues during meetings with your superiors. A nod here and there, along with the occasional 'I see', and 'sure' tells them that you are paying attention, and helps you sustain your focus as well.

Listening is more than just hearing words. Moving past that and using it as a means to build genuine connections is the beginning of effective communication.

The Art of Speaking

The success of your communication all depends on how the other person responds to you. If you are understood differently from how you intend to be understood, then you have to consider that there's a degree of failure on your part.

We cannot control exactly how others will respond to us because they have their own viewpoints and biases. What we do have is a level of influence that we must maximise by first understanding others through active listening, and then using what we have learnt to choose our approach.

You cannot assume that you are communicating well simply because you are sure of your intentions. Your desire to give your patients the best treatment or to establish camaraderie among your colleagues loses its power when you are unable to successfully convey it.

A good way to start maximising the power of your words is by growing an awareness of your choices. How do you talk? What words do you use? Examine the things you usually say to your patients when they are difficult, and to your colleagues when your shift is challenging.

Julian Treasure, sound and communications expert, claims that people do not want to listen to you when you gossip, judge others, complain, make excuses, lie, and express your opinions as though they are facts.

If these are the attributes that make up your speech patterns, then you have to address them.

Robin Sharma said, 'Talk less, do more. Brag less, create more. Distract less, learn more. Gossip less, produce more. Take less, give more. Hate less, love more.'

The words you may want to use are those that relay optimism, gratitude, honesty, authenticity, and thoughtfulness towards the well-being of others. You will want to show others, especially your patients, that you can empathise with them.

Empathy is the key to a successful relationship with your patients. It's the ability to put yourself in their shoes so you can address their emotional needs.

Remember that most of the people you will treat won't have an objective medical view of their condition, may it be severe, chronic, or simply routine check-up. They will be coming into your clinic with a lot of uncertainty about their health.

When you recognize their fears and anxieties instead of dismissing them, they consider that a sign that they are receiving quality care. This is what makes empathy so vital in communication. If there's no empathy, there's no trust, and where there's no trust between a patient and a clinician, there's little chance of satisfactory care.

John Powell said, 'Communication works for those who work at it.'

There's no shortcut to curbing bad habits and forming new ones other than through practice. It's by training yourself daily that you become a good communicator. Whenever you are tempted to complain or insist on your opinions, consider instead to be silent. Put in the conscious effort to find things to be optimistic about and shift your attention to those things.

Make it a point also to use conversational and inclusive language to create an atmosphere free of prejudice and discrimination. What you want is to acknowledge the other person's point of view to make them feel heard.

As you do all these, don't be afraid to let your personality shine through.

Les Brown said, 'Your smile will give you a positive countenance that will make people feel comfortable around you.'

When you freely show people your authentic self, then they'll also feel like they can open up and be transparent. They'll find you more relatable, and that's to your advantage as a clinician.

When you make this a habit, people will be more inclined to listen to what you have to say. That, in turn, makes it easier for your message to come across to them.

You will observe this when your patient agrees to the treatment or your professional advice because you've successfully communicated the value of what you are offering.

A mentee who needs correction will respond humbly because you have clearly expressed your intention to see him or her do better. Even a colleague who may be angry at you will be more inclined to forgive you when you are able to convey the sincerity of your apology.

There's a lot of internalisation, research, and practice that precedes this aspect of communication. Once you master this, though, you will see the positive impact it will have on your personal and professional relationships.

The Significance of Body Language

Nonverbal cues communicate the loudest. Even when you get the words right, your body language will reveal any lack of interest in your patient or confidence in a procedure.

You can assure your colleague that you are listening to what they are saying, but if you keep looking away and turning your body in another direction, they will know you are insincere. When the other person is faced with your mixed signals, there's a huge chance they'll believe your nonverbal cues instead of your verbal ones.

Body language broadcasts what you are truly feeling, and that's more difficult to control. This is why people will be more inclined to believe these than what you relay through words.

When you are able to combine the two, however, you achieve great results. Your rapport improves, which is paramount for any clinician, and you come across with more clarity and authenticity.

American psychiatrist Milton Erikson increased his rapport with his clients through a method called Matching and Mirroring. It operates on the principle that people like people who are similar to them. You consciously build rapport by creating a commonality through body language.

Milton understood the power of tapping the subconscious of the person you are communicating with, and you do that by matching and mirroring them.

The efficiency of this method also relies on the fact that people judge you in a matter of seconds. Author and life coach Tony Robbins said, 'Style is more important than substance initially.'

He means that when you approach someone with a tone, tempo, volume, posture, and gesture that are similar to theirs, you make them like you enough to catch the substance of what you are communicating.

No matter how good the substance of your message, if no one is willing to listen, then it serves no purpose.

Try this the next time you are conversing with someone. Mirror the tone and pace they use. Reflect their facial expressions and repeat the terminologies they use. A person who speaks fast and makes wild gestures will like someone who converses in the same way. Likewise, a quiet person will engage in a topic more with someone who is just as meek or serious as opposed to someone who's overly energetic.

The more conscious you are of your body language and that of others, the better the rapport you will build, and the more authentic your communication will be.

Evaluate Your Communication Skills

How good are your current communication skills? It's through self-awareness that you understand how you are doing in this area and what improvements you can make.

Here are some questions you can answer to give you an idea:

- Do I listen more than I talk?
- Do I speak in specifics or abstractly?

- Do I control my body language when I'm talking with my patients and my colleagues?
- Am I careful with the tone I use?
- Am I making the effort to ensure that the way I say something corresponds to my message?
- Do I listen to understand or listen to respond?
- Do my patients respond well to treatment and show appreciation for my service?
- Do my colleagues, superiors, or mentees often misunderstand my message?

A helpful way to get an objective view of your current communication skills is to get feedback from patients. You can, for example, have a post consultation questionnaire that they can fill out.

People from your support network can also give you feedback on how you come across to others. Habits you perceive as positive might not appeal the same way to the people you converse with, which may lead to offense or misunderstanding.

I am confident in my communication skills because patients often tell me that I gain their trust almost instantly, usually within the first ten minutes of my interaction with them. I've invested considerable time and made a conscious effort to always develop this vital skill area. As should you.

Excellent communication is one element that separates the average clinician from the great clinician. For you to achieve your dreams, you must aim to perfect your communication skills.

Chapter 7

Leadership

The leaders who work most effectively, it seems to me, never say 'I.' They don't think 'I.' They think 'we'; they think 'team.'

Tom Peters

As you aim to become a great clinician, you will inevitably find yourself in a position of leadership. This is true even before you are officially designated as one in your workplace. People are attracted to greatness, and when they see that in you, they gravitate towards your circle of influence.

Bear in mind that without you being aware of it, you are already leading your colleagues and mentees just by the way you think, speak, and act. You've started to cultivate the qualities of a good leader, although by far you've only been intentionally leading yourself.

And that's where the difference lies. Leadership must be done with intention. You do it with the awareness that you are capable of putting people in a better position to learn, grow, collaborate, and achieve goals individually and as a group.

You also have to commit to it because true leadership knows no retirement age. Once you take this role, you always have to remember that your words and actions have an impact on the people you are leading.

Commitment is integral because as you grow as a leader, you also develop an understanding that at its core, leadership is about putting people first. It's about serving others rather than exercising your authority to dictate their actions.

And this is the beautiful thing about leadership as a clinician: you amplify your capacity to serve patients because you lead people in your profession towards better service.

As a clinician, you are considered a leader by your nurse and admin staff within the clinic. Progress often means becoming the senior clinician, the one responsible for training junior colleagues and becoming an educator or mentor to the people around you.

In this chapter, I'll share with you my views on developing a leadership mentality, taking on opportunities to lead, and overcoming restrictions that can limit your circle of influence.

Leading by Example

People learn through observation. They pick up cues for acceptable behaviour and speech based on the example you set whether you are aware of it or not.

As you cultivate a leadership mentality, you have to make a thorough examination of how you present yourself and your values.

People will find it difficult to follow the work ethic you claim to believe in if they see you slacking off. Similarly, they'll feel they can break the dress code if they notice you doing so every now and then.

Your words matter only as much as your actions are able to follow through. If you are going to lead effectively, you will have to lead by example.

Start by identifying what values matter to you because just as they are the building blocks of your character, they'll also function as the foundation of your leadership. Your character and priorities will find their way to the people in your team or organisation.

It is not in my nature to criticise or complain about people because those lead to demotivation. I focus on the positives and take errors as opportunities to point out areas of improvements. When I see they've exerted the effort to make positive changes, no matter how small, I praise them.

We all want to feel significant, especially in our line of work. By offering honest and sincere praise, I give them that assurance and encourage a growth mentality.

If I need to correct someone, I do it in private. When you reprimand a person in front of others, they'll focus on what other people think instead of the point you are trying to get across. That's not only ineffective, it's also a sure way to instigate acrimony within your team.

Another point I consider of great value to my leadership, particularly when it comes to correcting people, is active listening. I've mentioned in the previous chapter the impact of paying attention when you communicate. This is especially crucial when you are a leader because you cannot expect to manage a group of people you don't know.

It's by paying attention that you will determine the approach that makes a person compliant to your guidance. The more familiar you are with their character and how they are likely to react, the better prepared you will be to admonish them in a way that will produce a positive response.

In the same way they commit mistakes from time to time, you, too, will have your fair share of blunders. Admit them and show that you are also learning. This is how you make them comfortable with assuming responsibility because they are aware that when they do, they'll be met with support instead of criticism.

I will not expect something from them that I will not first show. It's unfair to think that they should forgive my errors in spite of my unwillingness to do the same for them. My aim is to set a standard, meet it, and then help them live up to it. That's how I earn my team's trust and respect.

Even when you encounter people who refuse to follow your example, you should continue to live out your values. Stay true and consistent because a leader is not moved by others' opinions. A leader is the one who moves others with his character.

Leading & Collaborating

I am leading my own team in my clinic. I'm there once a week, and this puts me in a challenging position. Once I put protocols in place, I have to rely on teamwork for everyone to deliver with excellence.

Leadership and teamwork go hand-in-hand. It's not enough that you influence positively. You need to work together with them to nurture the kind of collaboration that breeds results.

Healthcare is an industry where good teamwork is the result of multidisciplinary professions coming together to achieve a common goal—to help the patient. When you establish collaboration as a culture in your workplace, you reduce medical errors and improve patient safety.

This also helps you prevent burnout at work. People who know they can depend on others to assist them with their tasks are less likely to feel overwhelmed. Since everybody's jobs are interconnected, you can look out for each other to make sure that each one accomplishes their part in the big picture.

But teamwork is more than just being accountable for one another's output. As a leader, you can create an environment that's enjoyable without compromising the work ethic or standard you've set. You spend the majority of your time at work, after all. If they don't find any form of comfort or joy in being there, it's difficult to sustain a good performance or ensure that they'll stay for long.

You don't want them too comfortable, though, that they don't find it challenging.

Just as you set visions and goals for yourself, set some for your team as well. People like to be part of a bigger picture and know that their work amounts to something.

Champion basketball coach Pat Riley said, 'Teamwork requires that everyone's efforts flow in a single direction. Feelings of significance happen when a team's energy takes on a life of its own.'

Direction adds value to teamwork. Impart your vision with them and enable them to make it their own.

When Nelson Mandela was younger, he went to tribal meetings with his father. He noted that they sat in a circle and his father, being the leader, always spoke last.

This method ensured that everybody's opinions were heard and understood. Once it's his turn to speak, he summarizes all of their points before sharing his own, subtly guiding them towards the direction he intends to take.

There's an art to leadership that lets you carry your team along in a single direction, with everybody onboard capturing your team vision as their own.

Leading Through Partnerships

Leaders benefit from partnerships. People and organisations will come your way with opportunities for you to grow your circle of influence and saying yes to them takes you to a new level of leadership.

My partnership with other leaders in the industry has propelled my business. I have lectured for industry partners nationally and internationally and I have had access to their latest innovations prior to release dates. They help promote my brand. It's a reciprocal partnership.

It's through partnerships like this that I'm able to give more of my time and expertise to people who are not directly under my team or sphere of influence.

Robert Cialdini introduced the Rule of Reciprocation in his book *Influence: The Psychology of Persuasion*, where he says that it's human nature to want to repay what another person has given us.

Zig Ziglar sums up the point of this claim when he said, 'You will get all you want in life, if you help enough other people get what they want.'

Our individual ladders to success are interconnected, and as a leader, I ensure that I keep an eye on my colleagues and staff. Not to judge how far behind another person is, but to check who needs help climbing up. Other people - leaders in their own right - have done the same for me, and I pay it forward by reaching out to those who need it.

Leading Beyond Limits

At the time of writing this book, I am in a government-mandated quarantine due to the COVID-19 pandemic. I continue to give webinars and do live broadcasts on social media.

Nobody found it convenient or easy when our day-to-day lives were interrupted, and a global health crisis emerged. People were talking about a "new normal" and we all had to find ways to regain our momentum in spite of the restrictions.

I decluttered my loft and converted it into an office creating an inviting and comfortable environment to work from. The immediate result is that I am more productive and I look forward to being in there to complete the tasks I'd set for myself. My environment plays a crucial role in how I think and behave, so I took control of it at once and turned it into an opportunity.

It was challenging, but my vision kept me going. My sense of purpose drove me to do what I can to continue sharing my knowledge and leading other clinicians to provide quality care.

Dale Carnegie said, 'If you believe in what you are doing, then let nothing hold you up in your work. Much of the best work of the world has been done against seeming impossibilities. The thing is to get the work done.'

Renowned physicist Stephen Hawking is a prime example of leading beyond limits. He was diagnosed with amyotrophic lateral sclerosis (ALS) at the age of 21. His doctor gave him five years to live, but he exceeded that and died at the old age of 76. He not only surpassed the medical limitations imposed by his disease - he lived long enough to make great contributions to humanity's knowledge about the universe.

True leaders will always find ways to fulfil their purpose no matter what stands in their way. Be the first to step up and say to everyone that it can be done, and then, just as Roger Bannister disproved the four-minute mile barrier, people will follow in your footsteps.

Leading and Learning

Your leadership style will mature with you. As you keep on learning and fine-tuning your skills, you will develop approaches that will help you adapt to the crowd and environment you are dealing with.

Whenever I provide feedback to a colleague, I use the well known technique described as a Feedback Sandwich. This basically means starting on a positive note, inserting the negative, and then ending on another positive note. It revolves around the concept of reducing the blow of the negative by wrapping it with a reminder of how much I value their strengths and contributions.

It works with junior colleagues well, but not so much with seniors when used too often. I find that the impact lessens, and I have to find another means to get the same result.

Develop a style that matches your own personality. Be authentic and make sure it comes from the right place. Remember that it is a dialogue, not a monologue. When you've made your point, be prepared to listen and understand what the other person has to say.

It's particularly useful for you to remember this because if you want to know how you are doing with regards to leadership, your first course of action should be to ask for feedback.

Principles author Ray Dalio points out that our brains, by default, perceive feedback about our shortcomings as an attack. The rational part of our brains, however, wants to hear this feedback so it can be used as a basis for improvement.

You cannot address a weakness you are unaware of. It's not having weaknesses that make you a bad leader, it's ignoring them to protect your emotions and self-esteem that make you one.

Request feedback from your team as well as from your mentors. Create a culture that sees this practice as a means to improve rather than to pull you down.

Your openness to receive feedback sends a message that you are willing to accept your blind spots and grow from them. That's the kind of leader people want to follow.

John J. McCloy said, 'Humility leads to strength and not to weakness. It is the highest form of self-respect to admit mistakes and to make amends for them.'

Lead with humility. It's the attitude that will bring you closer to your greatness.

Chapter 8

The Importance of Mentorship

'If I have seen further, it is by standing on the shoulders of giants.'

Isaac Newton

In Homer's *Odyssey*, Odysseus, King of Ithaca, had to leave home to fight in the Trojan War. He put the charge of his household to Mentor, who also served as a teacher and guide for his son, Telemachus.

Although fictional, there's wisdom in the king's decision to leave charge of his son to someone who can guide him, not just protect and oversee him. The prince bears responsibilities, and in order to fulfil them, someone has to stand beside him to show him the way.

Today, we're more exposed to finite connections with coaches who come and go in our lives. We look to social media and the web for tutorials and answers.

While those methods do help, they can't replace the value of a mentor.

Unlike a coach, a mentor is a person with whom you develop a long-term relationship aimed at assisting your growth. It's someone who imparts you with wisdom and knowledge and actively supports and contributes to your endeavours.

John Wooden said, 'Mentors are available at all stages of your leadership life - early, middle, and late. Seek them out and listen; absorb their knowledge and use it.'

Every clinician needs a mentor to amplify and fast-track their success. If you haven't connected with any yet, this chapter will give you reasons to look for one and, in the future, be one yourself.

The Value of a Mentor

The people you surround yourself will impact your mindset either positively or negatively, and this ultimately affects how you behave. Environment, mindset, and behaviour are all linked.

Stephen Covey said, 'Always surround yourself with people who are more talented and competent than you.'

Having a mentor creates a shift in your environment and puts you in a position of continuous awareness and desire for growth. More than just surrounding yourself with someone who's more skilled and more experienced, you develop a relationship that allows you to stand beside them and receive instruction.

A lot of clinicians do not have a mentor at times when they would benefit most from having one. It is crucial to have one at the beginning of your career, someone you can shadow and learn from, especially about things that dental school will not teach you.

I met my first mentor back in 2012 when I was a visiting sedation dentist for a clinic.

He is a well-known dentist, and I had heard about him previously through the dental community. I only had the privilege of getting to know him, though, when we both became involved in a dental partnership.

In 2014, I amalgamated my small dental referral clinic with a group of clinics that my mentor was building with other colleagues.

The rest is history. Once I left my full-time medical training position, I came on board with the partnership.

I had a natural inclination to learn from this person, as he was the clinician carrying out all the implant work for our dental clinics.

Initially, I helped him and observed his work on implant cases. He did this once a week, and I would be by his side observing what he was doing. It was an immense opportunity to hone my knowledge and skills as I assisted him with many cases over a number of years.

To learn from him on a one-to-one basis had a monumental impact on my professional growth.

Over time, I became his apprentice. He opened opportunities for me first by allowing me to do the initial consultations.

Then, sometimes, I would sedate the patients and assist with the surgeries. As time went by, he entrusted me with more responsibilities, and my confidence grew. I then went on to manage some cases on my own. Everything was done in a stepwise manner in terms of progressing to more complex procedures.

Benjamin Franklin said, 'Tell me and I forget, teach me and I may remember, involve me and I learn.'

Mentorship, when done right, gives you a level of involvement that allows you to grow at a steady pace. Having a mentor by my side during surgeries benefited my confidence because he enabled me to experience new things at a pace that matched my skills. At the same time, there was a consistent challenge to step up because I saw how good he was at his work.

Mentors will have an objective view of your progress, and because they have your best interest at heart, you can trust their opinion. It's easy to overestimate or underestimate your skills when you don't hear an outside perspective, and either of that can lead to unfavourable consequences. The former can put you in a situation you are not equipped to handle, and the latter can keep you from pursuing new things that you are capable of succeeding at.

If you think you can manage a complex procedure but your mentor disagrees, they will tell you why so you can proceed to take the steps to qualify. Likewise, if you are skilled but lacking in confidence, it's your mentor who will provide timely encouragement that will push you out of your comfort zone.

Bob Proctor said, 'A mentor is someone who sees more talent and ability within you than you see in yourself, and helps bring it out of you.'

Bringing out the best in you also entails giving you caution when due. They'll share their mistakes with you so that you don't have to experience them first-hand to learn from them. They'll share the lessons they've picked up along the way, and it's your job as a mentee to utilize them to go further and generate better results.

Having a mentor is valuable. It's not a sign of weakness or proof that you are less capable than your peers. In fact, many great people in history boast of having mentors who guided their way.

When you seek one, you actually exhibit your maturity and relentless drive for success.

Pursuing Mentorship

A few years later I met the next person who played a major role in my career development. I crossed paths with him in South Africa in 2016. We happened to be on a course together, and we hit it off right away.

We kept in touch after returning to the UK, and he invited me to come and watch him work. I travelled to the north of Wales where his practice is based. He allowed me to watch and, sometimes, assist him in procedures.

His generosity with his knowledge astonished me. He shared with me his insights and the reasoning behind his methods, and we'd reflect on cases together.

He gave me a lot of advice and showed interest in helping me advance my career.

Before I knew it, he started mentoring me. He was focused on full arch and complex grafting procedures, and he made time to educate me further on these.

Later, I discovered that his generosity encompassed not only his time and knowledge, but also the opportunities that came his way.

As his career progressed, he carried me along by opening new doors for me. I was able to take over the position at the clinic he was working in. Through that, I increased my exposure to implant work.

He also opened the doors to some industry partners I work with today.

He was kind enough to allow me to attend courses with him as a delegate, and then as an assistant on his course. Over time, I became a part of the faculty and involved in teaching on the course.

I would teach on three or four courses a year, and being around high-calibre dentists allowed me to grow my community. Since I have been mentored by him, my growth has been colossal.

As you continue to pursue your vision, you will inevitably come across people who are as passionate as you. Some of them will be your mentors, and each individual who takes up that role in your life has something unique to offer.

John C. Maxwell said, 'The best way a mentor can prepare another leader is to expose him or her to other great people.

A good mentor will share their network with you, thus connecting you to people or industries that can propel your professional growth. They'll want to teach you what worked for them and guide you as you walk the same path.

Their leadership is valuable in achieving your goals, so it's important that they know exactly what your vision is and how you want to get there.

Another reason it's good to share your goals with your mentor is to allow them to hold you accountable. There are times when you will find it difficult to motivate yourself, but by having a mentor to point you back to your dreams, will make you more likely to take action.

Mentors and Heroes

As I look forward to the next decade, I reflect on my career to date. I am lucky enough to have mentors and heroes who have helped me get to where I am today.

It's beneficial to your journey to have people you look up to, regardless if you know them personally or not. This is why, apart from my mentors, I also have heroes.

A mentor is someone who provides individualised guidance and takes a personal interest in you.

A hero is someone publicly visible that anyone can follow.

There are many people out there who have been running this race longer than I have. Some of them are in my profession and others aren't. I follow these people because there are numerous lessons to be learned from their individual journeys that can make mine faster and easier.

Gina Greenlee said, 'Experience is a master teacher, even when it's not our own.'

Fastrack your career by avoiding years of trial and error. Find mentors and identify heroes in your respective fields; they will guide you, and that is the quickest way to success.

The very purpose of this book is to accomplish that for you—to teach you through my own experiences and pass down the lessons I've learned from my mentors.

Napoleon Hill said, 'It is literally true that you can succeed best and quickest by helping others to succeed.'

As a mentor myself, I like to share the success of my mentees. To see you, mentees, doing well and exuding confidence is gratifying.

Go ahead and read this book again. Pick up as many lessons as you can and then apply them to your life. Consider these tools that will prepare you to do things better and faster than I have, and then pass the knowledge to your own mentees. Tell your own story to equip them for the future.

I look forward to a time when all clinicians look out for each other this way, inviting people to stand on their shoulders so that all our dreams and all our efforts amount to a big picture that benefits everyone in the healthcare industry and the people we serve.

Chapter 9

Giving Back: My Charity Work

'The best way to find yourself is to lose yourself in the service of others.'

Gandhi

The 2005 Kashmir Earthquake displaced over 3.5 million people and claimed the lives of 90,000. Many of the deceased left behind children with no home and no family to take care of them.

It's difficult to imagine how the collision of tectonic plates can change lives so drastically over the course of hours. It must've been more perplexing to young minds that have barely scratched the surface of life, and in an instant were forced to face the devastating truth about loss.

When Dental Aid Network (DAN) organized a mission trip in October 2016 to provide free treatment for the orphans of Kashmir Orphans Relief Trust (KORT), there was no question about my participation. Charity is a lesson my father instilled in me through his own actions. He never had much, but he made a conscious effort to give to the people who had less.

I knew I had something to give: my expertise, time, energy, and heart. When the opportunity arose to extend what I had to these children, I grabbed it.

Charity is A Challenge

Fulfilment isn't the only emotion you will feel when you volunteer on dental aid mission, although it is the prevailing one. Long hours of hard work start from the planning stages, when we recruit volunteers - core clinicians, nurses and therapists - and map out the logistics.

Over 200 orphans received essential dental treatment in our 2016 trip to Kashmir. Many of those children had never received treatment before, let alone visited a dentist. We also lent our services to two local schools for children suffering from blindness and hearing impairments.

We began by screening them and planning treatments, organising them by age groups and prioritising those with urgent care needs. The treatments we carried out included fillings, extractions, periodontal treatment, and oral care instruction.

Our clinic opened at nine in the morning and closed at five in the afternoon. The mission itself took six clinical days filled with different encounters with different children, all of whom were glad for the treatment.

Trips like this allow you to develop a sense of pride for what you do, especially when you see the smiles on their faces. Every now and then, however, there's an itch of frustration for what you cannot do for them and how much more you want to give but can't.

I knew when I volunteered for the charity set up by my friends from Glasgow that dental aid missions would not be simple. Our vision to help children in areas of conflict aims to resolve the shortage of dental care around the world.

The dental aid missions are self-funded. We use the money we raise to buy the materials needed for the missions. Thankfully, partnering with other charities like Kashmir Orphans Relief Trust (KORT), Palestinian Children's Relief Fund (PCRF), and Penny Appeal enables us to do our work more efficiently.

I have been on dental aid missions to Kashmir and Palestine twice. We have also assisted in orchestrating trips to Greece and Gambia.

Charity is not a holiday, even when we go to these beautiful places. What I've gleaned from years of committing myself to this work is that giving back transcends the physical.

It is a holiday for the soul.

Do It Anyway

I am driven by the desire to give back, and I hope that by the end of this book, I have persuaded you to do the same.

I am fortunate for the many opportunities I have enjoyed in my life and I don't want to take those for granted. Neither should any of you. If you've had access to education, a roof above your head, a circle of good people, and a job in the medical field, you have enough reason to join me in my campaign to pay it forward. The best way we can do that is to utilise our professional training to help the most vulnerable individuals in society.

I elaborated on the challenges of charity work because it shouldn't be sugar-coated. There will be sacrifices and inconvenience in the name of good work. Do it anyway.

When you help children and see that you have made a difference, no matter how small it seems, you gain an experience that no money can buy. It's life-changing not only for those you help, but also for you.

The past couple of years have been difficult for me in terms of volunteering because I have a young family.

I plan to teach my children the same lessons that my father taught me. When circumstances permit, we plan to go together on charity aid missions in the future. I look forward to sharing with them the joy I feel whenever I give back.

There are also other joys to be found in charity work:

- You meet like-minded people whose ethos fortify and further your own;
- You collaborate with organisations and learn from their methods and visions regarding medicine and charity work;

- You create a network of foreign professionals, experience their work environment, and share ideas;
- You get immersed in different cultures and get educated on the joys and hardships they experience.

My parents' heritage was a big influence on me during my formative years in Glasgow. The holidays in Pakistan, China, and Hong Kong to visit relatives exposed me to a diversity of vibrant cultures at a young age. Little did I know then that this exposure would benefit me in my encounters with a variety of people and communities during our dental aid trips.

Our goal to aid children in conflicted areas meant enduring some of their daily hardships, too. In Palestine, we worked in the city of Nablus and saw the restrictions Arabs faced, particularly with checkpoints regulating their travels.

My heart went out for them, but at the same time, I was consumed with gratitude for the liberties I enjoy living in the United Kingdom. As you go on your first, second, and tenth charity trip, I'm sure you will bring home lessons that will enrich your soul too.

The Proceeds

All the proceeds from this book will go to the Dental Aid Network charity.

There is only so much we need to live comfortable lives. Once you get there, what's next? The only financial action that has any significant merit moving forward is to extend my blessings to those who have so much less or even nothing.

My vision from the start has always been to use this book as a means to accomplish that, and I want you to know that you have contributed to this cause.

You've just helped change a person's life, and from the bottom of my heart, I thank you.

Connect with me:

Website: www.drferhanahmed.com

Email: info@drferhanahmed.com

Facebook: www.facebook.com/drferhanahmed

Instagram: www.instagram.com/drferhanahmed

LinkedIn: www.linkedin.com/in/drferhanahmed

Twitter: www.twitter.com/ferhan_ahmed